When Caring is Not Enough

Note

Health and social care practice and knowledge are constantly changing and developing as new research and treatments, changes in procedures, drugs and equipment become available.

The authors, editor and publishers have, as far as is possible, taken care to confirm that the information complies with the latest standards of practice and legislation.

When Caring is Not Enough

Examples of Reflection in Practice

edited by

Tony Ghaye and Sue Lillyman

QUAY
BOOKS

A division of MA Healthcare Ltd

Quay Books Division, MA Healthcare Ltd, St Jude's Church, Dulwich Road, London
SE24 0PB

British Library Cataloguing-in-Publication Data
A catalogue record is available for this book

ISBN-10: 1 85642 419 7
ISBN-13: 978 1 85642 419 6

Printed by CLE, Huntingdon, Cambridgeshire

Contents

Contents

Contributors

Heather Campbell *SRN, NDN, PWT, Cert Ed, BA (Hons) MSc*

I am an experienced educationalist who has worked in health and social care education since 1983. I have spent the last 15 years specialising in cancer and palliative care practice and education, leading palliative programmes at the Royal Marsden Hospital and now working as Head of Education in a hospice in the West Midlands. Interests include psycho-social and ethical issues in cancer and palliative care.

Val Chapman *PhD, MSc, Cert Ed, DIP RSA (SpLD)*

Val Chapman is Director of the Centre for Inclusive Learning Support at the University of Worcester. Her work in the area of Disability/Equal Opportunities in HE in the UK was recognised in 2004 by the award of a National Teaching Fellowship, and in 2005 by the designation of her Centre as a partner in the LearnHigher Centre for Excellence in Learning Teaching (one of 16 Higher Education partners). From September 2006 to 2007, she also held a UNESCO funded Chair in Special Education at Qatar University alongside her UW responsibilities.

In addition to her University roles, Val has been employed by the Quality Assurance Agency as a Subject Reviewer and Institutional Auditor. She was the Standing Conference of Principals (SCOP) representative on the Higher Education Funding Council for England (HEFCE) Students with Learning Difficulties and Disabilities (SLDD) Advisory Group, and sat on the Disability Rights Commission's Post 16 Reference Group advising on the development of the Code of Practice for the Disability Discrimination Act. A member of the Higher Education Academy's (HEA) former Disability Special Interest Group, she is currently on the steering group of the Higher Education Equal Opportunities Network (formerly chair, vice chair and treasurer and a member of HEFCE's Leadership Foundation in Higher Education Diversity Advisory Group.

Val has published quite widely and has presented at numerous conferences, frequently as an invited speaker, both in the UK and overseas.

Tony Ghaye *Cert Educ, BEd (Hons), MA (Educ), PhD*

I am a positive psychologist and have worked at the interface of healthcare and practice improvement for much of my life. I am now the Director of Reflective Learning International, a social enterprise that promotes and delivers a special kind of strengths-based reflective practice. In my working life I have been fortunate in being able to work with and learn from a very wide range of professionals, such as nurses, GPs, social workers, police, probation officers, therapists of various kinds, teachers and coaches. I have also had the privilege and challenge of working with individuals, organisations and communities in the Third World, mainly in East Africa. This experience has energised my commitment to inter-professional learning and multidisciplinary working to help to improve what we do, with and for others. I am the founder and Editor-in-Chief of the Routledge Taylor & Francis international and multidisciplinary journal called *Reflective Practice*, which publishes six issues per year.

Josephine Hamilton-Jones *BSc (Hons), Tech, PhD*

I grew up in Sheffield, South Yorkshire, in an academic, music and sports-orientated environment. I gained a degree in Mathematics and its Applications at University of Wales Institute of Science and Technology, Cardiff, in 1983 and completed my doctorate in 1987, considering the strategies used to solve battle equations and employing these methods to solve equations in epidemiology. With a young family, I moved into further education and lectured in mathematics, computing and information technology at several colleges around the country, rising to management level. Since 1994, I have been an examiner, mentor and tutor in quantitative methods for the National Extension College to home and international students studying degrees through distance learning.

I returned to Higher Education in 1997 to pursue my research interests in simulation, modelling and the use of IT for teaching and learning. I lecture in Information Technology and Computer Modelling at University College Worcester.

Ruth Hardie *RGN*

Since qualifying in 1985 I have gained a wide range of nursing experience in a variety of fields. As Matron of a Hospice I believe that there needs to be strong nursing leadership to empower my staff to give high-quality nursing care. I studied for my MSc at University College Worcester. My interests are in critical reflective practice, effective communication, patient autonomy and interdisciplinary teamwork, maintaining that you need all of these aspects to ensure that patients receive the most appropriate care and staff reach their full potential.

Sue Lillyman *MA, BSc (Nursing), RGN, RM, DPSN, PGCE (FAHE)*

Having qualified as a Registered General Nurse in 1980 and Midwife in 1983 I worked within various areas, including intensive care, gynaecology and care of the elderly, rehabilitation and acute medicine until entering nurse education in 1989. I have worked as a Senior Lecturer and faculty Head of Quality Assurance within Birmingham City University and currently as Senior lecturer at the University of Worcester. I took three years out working with street children and delivering medical services to villagers in remote villages in the Amazon in Peru before returning to the UK and continuing with my career in healthcare education. My teaching responsibilities have been with post-registration nurses undertaking diploma, degree and masters courses in nursing and collaborative community care Masters course for healthcare workers. Specialist areas of interest include care of the elderly, reflective practice, competence in practice, critical thinking and professional issues.

Sarah Mann *RGN, BSc (Hons)*

I worked in the Endoscopy Unit at the Alexandra Hospital in Redditch. Prior to this I worked for 18 months on Endoscopy at Heartlands Hospital in Birmingham. My present post involves the provision of therapeutic and diagnostic gastroscopy, colonoscopy, bronchoscopy and ERCP for both in- and outpatients. The work involves the physical and psychological preparation of patients, providing assistance to the medical staff and the recovery and advising of patients before discharge. I am involved in the day-to-day management of the unit, ensuring the smooth running of the lists and planning for unscheduled procedures. My interest in training and teaching has enabled me to develop an in-house training plan for use on the endoscopy unit and to be actively involved in the training of staff new to the unit. I find the post a challenging one and hope to be able to develop my role of nurse, manager and teacher.

Helen Taylor *BSc (Hons) Nursing, PGCE, RGN*

I read for a degree in nursing at Leeds Polytechnic, with a registered nurse qualification. I retrained as a secondary school teacher, specialising in biology and integrated science, at the University of Bristol. Until recently I have been combining researching for a PhD with part-time nursing. While studying for my PGCE I developed an interest in child health and health education in schools. I am married with two small sons and live in Worcestershire.

Acknowledgements

In the preparation of the new edition of this book we acknowledge with deep appreciation the insightful contributions of our original writers and welcome the wisdom of our new contributors. Additionally we wish to acknowledge all our colleagues, who work in various healthcare contexts, in both developing and emerging nations, and who have inspired us with their energy, dedication and commitment to caring for others.

Introduction

Sue Lillyman and Tony Ghaye

Healthcare literature provides us with a wealth of information and examples of how reflection can be used within our clinical practice. Many authors over the past two decades have identified how it can be used to develop practice (Loughram, 2002), improve critical thinking (Teekman, 2000), build new theories (Korthagen and Lagerwerf, 2001), justify practice (Ghaye and Lillyman, 2010), change and enhance practice (Johns, 2004), help us to develop a level of self-awareness (Ostermann and Kemp, 1993), learn through practice (Burnard, 1988; Jarvis, 1992; Coutts-Jarman, 1993; Johns, 1995) and celebrate our practice (Ghaye, 2010). For the majority of healthcare professionals it has also become a professional requirement for practice. Therefore in this second edition of the book *Caring Moments* we have tried to include those examples of practice from a variety of settings where people have used different approaches to reflection that help to capture some of the aspects noted above. We have, however, also altered the title to *When Caring is Not Enough* to emphasise a commitment to caring as well as a questioning of it, and so emphasise the value of reflection in everyday practice.

We can see how we can make sense of our practice by including different examples of practice and using different approaches to reflection by linking three ideas together. These are reflection-on-practice, the meanings of the term *discourse*, and the use of story and experience. In Chapter 2 the stories in this sense are value-laden stories. They have also been stories told mainly through a qualitative medium. But in Chapter 11 we use numbers to make the point that we can develop a storyline in very different ways – ways other than in words alone. Chapter 11 also serves to make the point that we all have preferred ways of creating a story. Creating it with numbers and words is not everyone's preference, but it is arguably a very important one with the developing healthcare technologies in the new millennium. In this book we have not exploited poetic, visual, musical, still and video forms (Prosser, 1998), 3D modelling and other art-based forms

(Pratt and Wood, 1998), verbal and nonverbal processes, concept mapping and so on. We have suggested that we need the courage to explore them, as all of these can, for certain individuals and groups, be important catalysts to help make sense of practice. They are media through which we can express ourselves and something with which we can work and engage. We have also made the point that the story that is produced, as well as the process of story-making and telling, are important. Additionally, and in the first book in this series (Ghaye and Lillyman, 2010), we learnt that merely having experience is not enough. What counts is what we do with it. In this book we hope that we have shown what can be done with experience set out in a story form. Learning through reflection is paramount here.

A number of things might usefully be considered by those wishing to engage in reflective writing of the kind presented in this book. These have been set out in the first chapter.

Quality care: an elusive idea?

Redfern and Norman (1990) suggest that quality care is the right of all patients and that it is the responsibility of the nurse who delivers it. It is through the chapters in this book that many of the characteristics and qualities of care are illuminated. To understand this better we have invited each author to 'frame' their thinking and contribution by focusing their attention on the selection and exploration of what we have referred to as a 'caring moment'. This has been further developed in Chapter 3, where the connections between caring moments and critical incidents are discussed. Sadly, 'good quality' care within a healthcare setting is often only defined by its absence. Arguably, therefore, there is a need to identify what is meant by good quality care for the individual, group and organisation. This will include reference to its clinical, professional and political dimensions. The concept of quality care, according to Benner (1996), can be traced back to Socrates (469–399 BC) and Hippocrates in 460–370 BC where the latter tried to move folk wisdom into a significant art of healing. The earliest written health records, according to Marr and Giebang (1994), were in the Babylonian Empire circa 1700 BC where sanctions were described for providing poor quality healthcare, and later through Florence Nightingale (1859), who introduced the idea of caring for patients by putting them in the best environment for nature to act upon them. Henderson (1960) suggests that nursing care should be done for the benefit of the patient and that care is administered to assist the patient to health or a peaceful death. Care is not just related to cure. It is a much more complex idea than this. The contributions to the book illustrate this vividly.

Caring is identified by the World Health Organization (1996) as an important part of nursing practice. Among other things they note that care needs to be understood in terms of relationships, for example with an individual, family or community. These views of care are demonstrated throughout the various chapters. Care is also associated with the notion of 'helping'. Helping includes creating a climate of healing, providing comfort, establishing a relationship and committing oneself to this relationship through that nursing care. Williams (1998) takes this further in his attempt to identify what we mean by 'quality nursing care' and suggests that it relates to the perceived degree to which patients' physical, psychological and 'extra care' needs are met. He suggests that physical needs are identified in relation to the lack of personal independence in daily physical function. Psychological needs relate to the supportive role assumed by the carer, including communication, providing information and being the patient's advocate. With regard to 'extra care needs' he suggests that this is difficult to define, but is concerned with the personal touch administered during the period of care.

Astedt-Kurki and Haggman-Laitila (1992) argue that some of the attributes of care are to do with nurses' attitudes, time for discussion, individualism, listening, showing interest in, feelings and understanding of the experiences of their clients/ patients. These attributes are developed further through the various chapters in the book. We should note that Phillips (1993) suggests that caring is a value-laden enterprise and that the intention of that care is often confused with achievements of the care. It is not the evaluation of care *per se*, but the means by which the individual draws on his or her knowledge, skills and attitudes to deliver that care, that identifies the values held. In other words, the caring values are evident in and through healthcare practice. Practice therefore needs to be understood as values-in-action.

Caring *vs.* cure

The role of the nurse or professional allied to medicine often identifies the role of 'caring' with emotional connotations, whereas the role of medicine is often associated with a curing function. Holden (1991) asks the question 'does the medical profession not care, and do carers not cure?' He notes the origins of the word 'care' and points out that it actually originates from the 11th century French word for 'cure'. He therefore questions if they should be seen as two separate identities or more appropriately in a more complex, interactive and holistic relationship? The important issue here is how healthcare professionals view their role, the emphases within it and the extent to which they feel able to live out their caring values in their practice.

Conclusion

The specific role that reflection plays within the delivery of a quality care service is demonstrated throughout this book and other related books (Ghaye and Lillyman, 2010). Reflection assists the individual in identifying and nourishing good practice. It can help us develop realistic action plans that serve to work at aspects of practice with the intention of trying to enhance and improve what we do. Reflection can also help us understand the difference between what we wish to do and what we are able to do as we try to care for our patients/clients. It can give us a better sense of self in relation to others, and the organisational contexts within which our practice is embedded. This book takes the notion of a caring moment as the essence and focus of healthcare work. The contributions describe different moments and use reflective practices to explore and make more sense of each one. In this way thinking and practice are helped to move forward. Without this reflective process we are doomed to relive the experiences and mistakes of the past. We enslave and imprison ourselves rather than provide ourselves with opportunities for enlightenment and empowerment.

References

Astedt-Kurkit, P. and Haggman-Laitila, A. (1992) Good nursing practice as perceived by client: a starting point for the development of professional nursing. *Journal of Advanced Nursing*, **17**, 1195–9.

Benner, P. (1996) *From Novice to Expert: Excellence and Power in Clinical Nursing*. Addison-Wesley, Menlo Park, CA.

Department of Health (1997) *The New NHS: Modern and Dependable*. HMSO, London.

Department of Health (1998) *A First Class Service, Quality in the New NHS*. HMSO, London.

Burnard, P. (1988) The journal as an assessment and evaluation tool in nurse education. *Nurse Education Today*, **8**, 105–7.

Coutts-Jarman, J. (1993) Using reflection and experience in nurse education. *British Journal of Nursing*, **2**(1), 77–80.

Ghaye, T. (2010) In what ways can reflective practices enhance human flourishing? *Reflective Practice*, **11**(1), 1–7.

Ghaye, T. and Lillyman, S. (2010) *Reflection: Principles and Practice for Healthcare Professionals*, 2nd edn. Quay Books, London.

Henderson, V. (1960) *The Nature of Nursing: A Definition and Its Implications for Practice, Research and Education*. Macmillan, New York.

Holden, R. (1991) In defence of cartesian dualism and hermeneutic horizon. *Journal of Advanced Nursing*, **16**, 1375–81.

Marr, H. and Giebang, H. (1994) *Quality Assurance in Nursing Concepts, Methods, Case Studies*. Campion Press Ltd, Edinburgh.

Jarvis, P. (1992) Reflective practice and nursing. *Nurse Education Today*, **12**(3), 174–81.

Johns, C. (1995) The value of reflective practice for nursing. *Journal of Clinical Nursing*, **4**, 23–30.

Johns, C. (2004) *Becoming a Reflective Practitioner*, 2nd edn. Blackwell Science, London.

Korthagen, F. and Lagerwerf, B. (2001) Teachers' professional learning: how does it work? In: *Linking Practice and Theory: the Pedagogy of Realistic Teacher Education* (ed. F. Karthagen), pp. 175–206. Lawrence Erlbaum, Mahwah, NJ.

Loughram, J. (2002) Effective reflection practice: in search of learning about teaching. *Journal of teaching Education*, **53**(1), 33–34.

Nightingale, F. (1859) *Notes on Nursing*. Harrison and Sons, London.

Ostermann, F. F. and Kottlamp, R. (1993) *Reflective Practice for Educators: Improving Schooling Through Professional Development*. Corwin Press, Newbury Park.

Phillips, P. (1993) A deconstruction of caring. *Journal of Advanced Nursing*, **18**, 1554–8.

Pratt, M. and Wood, M. (eds) (1998) *Art Therapy in Palliative Care: The Creative Response*. Routledge, London.

Prosser, J. (ed.) (1998) *Image-based Research: A Source book for Qualitative Researchers*. The Falmer Press, London.

Redfern, S. and Norman, I. (1990) Measuring the quality of nursing care: a consideration of different approaches. *Journal of Advanced Nursing*, **15**, 1260–71.

Teekman, B. (2000) Exploring reflective thinking in nursing practice. *Journal of Advanced Nursing*, **31**(5), 1112–35.

Williams, A. (1998) The delivery of quality nursing care: a grounded theory study of nurses' perspective. *Journal of Advanced Nursing*, **27**, 808–16.

World Health Organization (1996) *Report of the WHO committee Nursing Practice: WHO Technical Report Series 860*. WHO, Geneva.

CHAPTER I

Creating a caring moment

Tony Ghaye

Finding something significant to write about

This is more easily said than done. Practice is often so complex that it is difficult to disentangle one thing to focus upon. Alas – and all too frequently – the focus becomes that part of our work that we feel less happy about, which needs 'fixing' and fast. This has given reflection a bad name. While it is understandable that many of us reflect on things like this, reflective practice is not only about putting right the things that are perceived to be wrong! This is a serious danger. We should also spend some time reflecting on the good bits, the things we are pleased about, right now. If we fail to do this, what is good and right today may become less attractive tomorrow. The reason for this is simple. We work within a dynamic and fast-changing healthcare system. Therefore we cannot confidently assume that what is good today will be good tomorrow. Conversely, some less good and worrying things of today can become less significant and worrying in tomorrow's world. When creating a caring moment (a story) to learn from, we should consider at least two basic kinds: stories of celebration and stories of reconstruction. Both are stories that need to be created and should be heard. Both are stories that precipitate action, but action of different kinds. The first requires the kind of action that tries to nurture, preserve and nourish all that is good in that particular caring moment. The second requires the kind of action that has to try to improve (reconstruct) the existing situation as depicted in the story. Simply writing down a caring moment is not enough. Caring moments require us to act. Caring alone is not enough.

Allowing ourselves to be creative

Creating a caring moment is (or can be), as the phrase suggests, a creative experience. In one way this can be described as moving from something known (or something we claim to know) – that is to say the chosen aspect of practice – to something as yet unknown (practice retold in story form). For most people 'being creative' can bring with it some anxiety. But this need not necessarily get in the way, especially if you find yourself working with a skilled reflective practice facilitator.

Resist being stifled by conventions

Storying can be stifled by literary conventions. In my experience, some healthcare workers are more preoccupied with this than with seeing it as essentially a process of communication and learning. They worry more about their spelling, sentence construction, and writing in the first person (using 'I' and 'we') than anything else! I am often asked 'Do you really want me to write it like an essay?'. For some, these are real anxieties that often touch upon some deep-seated and pervasive difficulties about writing, about how to write and about positioning ourselves clearly within our own story. In this sense they have to be respected. Conventions are important. They need to be understood and used, but in the appropriate context.

Place the emphasis on communication

What we say and how we say it matter. Arguably creating a caring moment reflects a desire to discern and assign meaning to our work. So it is understandable that we might ask the question, 'What makes a "good" caring moment?'. They might have the following qualities. I have deliberately stated each one in a positive manner. A caring moment is:

- **Recountable**: This means that a chosen practice event (significant incident) can be identified and reasons given for its choice – that the events in the incident can be presented in some way and put in some kind of sequence to form a story line. We may recount alone or co-write. This is where storying becomes a collaborative experience.
- **Told in a particular way**: Not only do choices have to be made about what is told but also about how the story is communicated. It may be done amusingly, angrily, sarcastically, provocatively, suspiciously, confidently, hesitantly and so on. 'Stories are important only as told' (Cohler, 1991, p. 182). We may tell them to ourselves and/or to others. We may read our story out aloud, on our own, or in a group (to an audience) and with the help of others. We may draw upon some other media (see above) to help us tell our story. I would argue that the use of caring moments in helping us reflect-on-practice (therefore learning from them and trying to move forward) requires an 'optimistic orientation' .This means that by telling the story we give ourselves a chance of adding meaning to our lives, of establishing our 'preferred story' and, through persistence and curiosity, seeking out and constructing an 'alternative story'.

- **Followable**: A good story is one that can be followed. This is often a complex task and not as straightforward as it might sound. We may claim our story is 'followable'. Others may disagree. Striving to make ourselves understood seems rational and logical. But many of us can never claim that we know ourselves in a complete, coherent and uncomplicated way. We have many 'selves', not one self. We have fragmented stories to tell, not fully knowable ones. We often have to strive to make connections. These are often not clearly apparent. We need to work out the difference and the links between the extra-ordinary (exceptional) and the ordinary. For a story to be followable it needs to have some kind of coherence about it. Sometimes this is not easy to establish. I am also making an assumption that the storyteller actually wants the listeners (audience) to follow the story.

- **Likely to affect its audience**: This is also a tricky quality with a number of parts. In presenting our caring moment (telling our story) we need to have some idea of the effect we are trying to create, or that it might create, with its audience. However, 'If one's self-image depends upon how others react, it seems natural that narrators would want their audiences to understand and agree with them. Therefore most storytellers emphasise only those experiences and reasons that their audiences find plausible' (Rosenwald and Wiersma, 1983; Tolman, 1991), 'they tell their stories in genres that their audiences are likely to recognise' (Harding, 1992; Modell, 1992) and 'they explain away whatever their audiences might find inappropriate' (Ochberg, 2000, p. 110). The caring moments that we choose to recount and communicate do not just fill us (the audience) in on clinical events. They should not be seen merely as people telling us about themselves and what they have done. The act of telling can also be seen as a way in which the teller tries to create a relationship (of a particular kind) with the audience. But I said this was a tricky quality. The assumption I am making is that talking through a caring moment might be seen as a way of 'making connections' (with practice, with other colleagues, with the audience and so on). It might also be seen as a way of keeping us at bay. Language and the way we use it can do this. This dual quality of 'inviting the listener in' but also of 'pushing the listener away' is important to understand, especially in the context of clinical supervision (Ghaye and Lillyman, 2007). We should not accept the simple idea that everyone tries to make their story 'followable'. Some who present their story may not expect or even want their audiences to understand them. They may not wish their audience to understand them in the same way as they claim to understand themselves. They may think it foolish or inappropriate to present a clear and transparent story, particularly if they have any kind of doubts about the motives of the audience. But there is also something else that touches upon the connected qualities of a caring moment being 'followable' and affecting the audience.

■ **Likely to affect the storyteller**: We have tried to stress through the books in this series that reflection, of one kind or another, done in particular ways, can be upsetting, 'dangerous' and unleash a torrent of frightening feelings that can be overwhelming for those who are participating. Reflective practices may well be important, but it is important that they are done well. On the other hand, reflective practices such as storying can be therapeutic and emancipating. I am describing strong feelings here. For some the reflective experience then may be regarded as a cathartic one. Reflection can unlock human potential.

Give the therapeutic, emancipatory and empowering effects of storytelling a chance

The therapeutic benefits of storytelling were noted in the nursing literature more than 60 years ago (Bacon, 1933). More recently Banks-Wallace (1998), in discussing the emancipatory potential of storytelling in a group (which she called 'Sisters in Session'), outlined six possibilities. These were that storytelling helped to provide:

■ **Contextual grounding**: The story provides a context that helps to position or locate ourselves in the world. The context influences how we see ourselves and others, the choices we make and how we act. The context is like the canvas and frame upon which we paint a picture of practice.

■ **Bonding**: In her research with women of African descent living in the Seattle-Tacoma region of the USA, she claims that bonding with other group members was the most important function of storytelling.

■ **Validation and affirmation**: The stories that were shared and the reactions of the group (audience) were an important means of women validating themselves and their reality. 'Validation of negative aspects often was a prerequisite to being able to critically examine their lives and make decisions regarding necessary changes. Stories affirming joy and goodness... were uplifting and energising' (Banks-Wallace, 1998, p. 20).

■ **Venting and catharsis**: Using storytelling to vent emotions was important to the group. 'No one ever really talked about the "heaviness" of the topics being discussed. There were only a few times when someone cried.... Many cathartic stories focused on the pain and frustration associated with living in the US as a woman and person of African descent' (Banks-Wallace, 1998, p. 20).

- **Storytelling as an act of resistance**: This is the role that stories can play in exposing, challenging and confronting dominant structures, discourses, myths and stereotypes. It is a way in which, through the stories we tell, we can resist and critique the dominant storylines. These may be the storylines that come from males, medics, management, government ministers and so on.
- **Education**: The communication of caring moments (stories) can, over time, be a way of creating a special kind of practical wisdom. This is eloquently described by Tschudin (1999, pp. 14–15):

Telling stories is essential in reflective practice. What is important, however, is that we listen to the essence of what the person is saying rather than to what we want to hear. The patient who says, 'I am scared of this operation' is not heard if she gets an answer like, 'You'll be alright; this sort of operation is routine here and you have a good surgeon'. The patient needs to tell her story of fear: what the fear is, when it started, why it started and where it has led her. In stories of human suffering, we need to hear not so much the practical details as the untold and perhaps not yet understood meaning. In doing this, we are carrying out the essential work of any ethic: being receptive, relating to the other and responding in the most fitting way. In listening to others, we are sharing and expressing that we are 'with' them. In sharing, we become equal, and this allows us to be moral.

Caring moments are value-laden moments. Creating caring moments reflects our use of two kinds of values: our espoused values (what we say we do in our work) and our values-in-action (what we actually do). These are often not congruent. We say one thing and then end up actually doing something else. Sometimes we are not good at living out our values in our practice. So, creating a caring moment is not enough. Telling the story and listening respectfully to it are not enough. Acting upon it in some appropriate way might be. Just saying that we care is not enough. We have to act in a manner congruent with our espoused caring values. In short, we have to be prepared to learn something from each caring moment that is recounted to us. This might be about ourselves, each other, our patients and clients, treatments, the contexts in which our practice takes place and many other things.

Hopefully this book shows that creating and reflecting on each caring moment is not like trying to repair a faulty machine. Creating a caring moment – telling, listening and learning from it – is not finding out what has gone wrong and then setting about trying to repair it. The whole exercise is not about correcting deficits, inadequacies and malfunctions within us, the team we may be a part of and the organisation for whom we work. The process should be viewed more positively and optimistically than this. Creating and reflecting on 'caring moments' should be undertaken with patience, persistence, deliberation and delicacy. The learning that may arise from reflective practices, of one kind or another, needs to be given the chance to breathe and emerge. This might usefully be done in the spirit of 'co-exploration' (Monk *et al.*, 1997).

References

Bacon, F. (1933) Getting well with books. *American Journal of Nursing*, **33**(11), 1143–6.

Banks-Wallace, J. (1998) Emancipatory potential of storytelling in a group. *Image – the Journal of Nursing Scholarship*, **30**(1), 17–21.

Cohler, B. (1991) The life story and the study of resilience and response to adversity. *Journal of Narrative and Life History*, **1**(2–3), 169–200.

Ghaye, T. and Lillyman, S. (eds.) (2007) *Effective Clinical Supervision: The role of Reflection*, 2nd edn. Quay Books, London.

Harding, S. (1992) The afterlife of stories: Genesis of a man of God. In: *Storied Lives* (eds. G. Rosenwald and R. Ochberg). Yale University Press, New Haven.

Modell, J. (1992) Work, identity and narrative. In: *Storied Lives* (eds. G. Rosenwald and R. Ochberg). Yale University Press, New Haven.

Monk, G., Winslade, J., Crocket, K. and Epston, D. (1997) *Narrative Therapy in Practice: The Archaeology of Hope*. Jossey-Bass, California.

Ochberg, R. (2000) On being part of an audience. In: *The Researcher Experience in Qualitative Research* (eds. S. Moch and M. Gates). Sage Publications, London.

Rosenwald, G. and Wiersma, J. (1983) Women, career changes and the new self. *Psychiatry*, **46**, 213–29.

Tolman, D. (1991) Adolescent girls, women and sexuality: discerning dilemmas of desire. In: *Women, Girls and Psychotherapy* (eds. C. Gilligan, A. Rogers and D. Tolman). Harrington Park, New York.

Tschudin, V. (1999) *Nurses Matter: Reclaiming Our Professional Identity*. Macmillan, Basingstoke.

CHAPTER 2

Reflection-on-practice as a discourse

Tony Ghaye

Caring moments: stories and experience as discourse

This is a book of stories, powerful stories. Each of the caring moments presented can be understood as a kind of story. Telling stories is a way in which healthcare professionals make sense of practice. Making some sense of practice when the world seems to be forever turbulent, changing and chaotic is a real achievement. Reflection-on-practice is a fundamental ingredient: reflection being a sense-making process.

> Sense is crafted, put together with skill and care, not simply experienced as if prefabricated. We can see others, and occasionally ourselves, making sense in a way which does not seem to be conducive to productive action; it is not simply that sense is made or not made, but that there are consequences to the kind of sense that is made. Everyday sense-making is not a matter of trying to make total sense of everything. There are levels of sense with which we feel comfortable. Too much sense – too clear an understanding of everything around us – may be boring. (Wallemaq and Sims, 1998, p. 121)

To this we might add, too little sense – being unclear about what is happening around us – is a recipe for disillusion, stress and burnout.

In the literature on reflective practice we often see a reference made to reflection as a way of turning experience into learning (Boud *et al.*, 1998). But experience can also turn into stories (Driscoll, 1999a,b, 2000; Bowles, 1995; Vezeau, 1993). Over time, stories transform into experience. In this book the 'caring moment-as-story' is a central idea. The stories are of many sorts and told in different ways. This storytelling can be understood as a discourse in which the uniqueness of the persons involved and the situation are displayed (Harre, 1998). They are examples of what Schafer (1992, p. 25) describes as, 'persons constructing and revising their various experiential selves'. Reflection is the process which fuels this reconstruction and revision, for within the chapters 'moments' are first described and then reflected upon. In essence, the caring moments might usefully be seen as the way in which healthcare professionals experience others, how they experience themselves and how they display or express themselves to others and vice versa. Stripped down, they are about how I am to you and how you are to me.

In Ghaye and Lillyman (2010) we suggest that reflective practice might usefully be understood as a discourse. We say this because one outcome of reflection is a set of meanings, statements, stories and so on that produce a particular version of events. This is one way to understand the term *discourse*. Each caring moment is a particular version of events. They are a 'text' and a reflection on this. Each 'text' is some kind of socially constructed reality. However, they are also much more than this. They touch upon a number of important issues for healthcare professionals to consider. I have suggested what ten of these issues might be in this introductory chapter.

I. Single and multiple realities

The texts challenge us to consider the notion of multiple realities, rather than the singular reality that we all sign up to. We do not all see and understand the world in the same way. The caring moments invite multiple 'readings' and therefore open up the possibility of appreciating alternative realities. They reflect the idea that we need to actively construct our own realities. Making sense of practice is therefore about building meanings and constructing identities for ourselves within a cultural, historical, political and clinical context. The caring moments are personal realities. They are something the writers perceive, claim to know and believe. Personal realities all differ. In healthcare we should always ask questions of the kind, 'What reality?', 'Whose reality?' and 'Whose reality counts?'.

2. Dominant realities and discourses

They serve to remind us that just as there are dominant realities which are often top-down or centre-periphery transferred realities, there are also dominant dialogues or discourses. Some of these are very clear about what is to be understood as real and true. The discourse of technical rationalism (Schon, 1983) is still a dominant way of viewing the world for many healthcare professionals. It advertises its dominance and authority over other discourses, for example by separating theory from practice and relegating the healthcare professional to 'mere service provider' and 'technician'. For a more detailed discussion about these issues see Ghaye *et al*. (2000).

3. They celebrate and prioritise subjectivity

For some in healthcare there is a distrust of all forms of subjectivity. This manifests itself in many ways. For example, it is revealed in the question I am repeatedly asked by students, 'Is it really OK to write in the first person?' and in the obsession that some have with conducting enquiries into the clinical, managerial and professional aspects of their healthcare work that always seem to have to involve very large samples and huge quantities of data, with validity and reliability defined in positivistic terms and very general results. It also manifests itself in enquiries that only generate 'objective' knowledge, because this seems to carry with it a sense of certainty. I do not deny the value of knowledge of this kind for certain purposes. However, we should not forget that you can indeed get large messages from small samples. We should not lose sight of the fact that every time we make a move, or take a decision about what to do next, what to do with what we have gathered, what to write and what to leave out, we involve subjectivities or value judgements. The caring moments here serve, in a small but significant way, to reclaim the subjective as a legitimate way of telling. They challenge the hegemony of the objective.

4. What knowledge and whose knowledge?

These caring moments raise the question about what knowledge is worth knowing. Taking responsibility for one's own future development and working in a safe and accountable manner is dependent upon our ability to reflect upon our own practice and that of others. Creating and reflecting on those aspects of our work that might be called 'caring moments', is a way of doing this. In addition to the principal modes through which the nursing profession, for example, has historically acquired knowledge (through tradition, authority, borrowing, trial and error, role modelling and mentorship; Ghaye *et al*., 1996) we can now legitimately add another. This is the personal, practical knowledge acquired through a reflection on the caring moments that constitute practice.

5. In whose voice?

Elsewhere we have argued (Ghaye and Lillyman, 2010) that reflective practices need to start where we are or feel we are. That in trying to enhance thinking, practice and the clinical environment we need to invite colleagues to present, and perhaps rediscover and redefine, their particular view of some healthcare issue they wish to reflect upon. Then they might usefully question how they currently respond to this (Freire and Faundez, 1989). This whole process requires the creation of some kind of 'text' which is the raw material that we use in the reflective process. In this book we have called these texts 'caring moments'. These moments have been 'produced' from the lived experiences of the contributors. So the point made by Fine and Weis (1998, p. 27) is highly relevant, namely, 'In whose voice do we write? Well, of course, our own'. This collection of moments enables us to hear the voices of those caring for others. It helps us understand their frames of reference, or perspectives on healthcare issues. The word 'voice' implies having something to say and a language to say it in. The languages used in this collection of caring moments attempt to evoke, in the reader, a sense of 'being there' too. All the 'moments' are reflected upon in different ways. In this sense they display an openness of spirit and an enquiring mind. These are surely qualities of the reflective practitioner.

6. The importance of experience

Working with experience is a central feature of reflective practice. Each caring moment is a special configuration of experience, thought about and told in a particular form. They represent the experiences of the self (and others). They are a source of knowledge and a valuable resource from which to learn. Johns and Freshwater (1998) go on to argue that they are also part of a 'transformative process'. Perhaps then we should be encouraging more healthcare professionals to tell their stories in this manner? Caring moments are about self: self in relation to others, experiences and a developmental process, all historically and culturally located and energised through reflective practices.

7. Have I told it as it really was – and does it matter?

These caring moments are retrospective accounts of healthcare, of some significance to the writers. The writers make themselves, and another, principally, the object of reflective examination. Constructing each moment has been a meaning-making process. Meaning is there, or perhaps more accurately 'in there' waiting to be re/discovered through reflection-on-action. We are of course making a big assumption here. The assumption is that these caring moments can indeed be captured and represented in a story or narrative form depicting events and life 'as it really was' (Usher, 1998). We should question any belief that these moments are indeed literal representations of what happened, was said and was felt. It is perhaps better to see them as a kind of 'fabrication', a 'reconstruction and presentation (rather than a representation) of the self through the process of textual inscription'

(Usher, 1998, p. 19). In other words, they are 'literary' rather than 'literal'. You may feel that at the end of the day this might not matter. If each caring moment may not be regarded as life as it really was and experienced, then I suggest we can see them as moments understood at a particular time and in a particular way and re-presented in a story form. A more pertinent question might be, 'So, what can we learn from reflecting on these stories-as-reconstructions?' Here critical forms of reflection (Day, 1999; Ghaye and Ghaye, 1998) are so important. By this I mean learning from each moment by standing back from it and asking, at least, 'How and why did that incident come about?'. *Critical* can be understood therefore 'to mean a relatively simple attitude... in which nothing is taken as necessarily given' (Tripp, 1998, p. 37). This critical attitude towards healthcare also invites us to ask the question, 'Whose interests are being served and how?'. From this kind of critical reflection we might see and be able to grasp the opportunity of enhancing thinking and clinical practice.

8. The importance of workplace culture

Each caring moment is situated within an historical, cultural, political and clinical context. They should not be seen as some kind of 'free-floating incidents', coming from nowhere. Each 'moment' needs to be understood in a context. That context can be generally referred to as a workplace or organisational context. When healthcare professionals work together for any length of time, for example within a unit, department, 'home', Trust and so on, they begin to come to know and to share certain values about what is right, proper, appropriate, sensitive, safe and ethical. Over time, patterns of behaviour reflect these values. These values and the values-in-action constitute the 'culture' of the workplace or organisation (Thompson, 1997). Each caring moment illustrates both values held and values-in-action. But they also reflect four other important things.

First, within the notion of workplace culture is the idea of power. Power is related to our potential or ability to do something or make something happen. It is derived from the relationships and interactions between healthcare professionals who operate within the 'structures' that serve to give the organisation its identity, serve its mission and sustain it. Each 'moment' has a power dimension within it defined in this sense.

Secondly, there is a political dimension to each caring moment. This is the way in which individuals or groups utilise power to influence values and actions. It is also about who gets what, where and how out of the 'moment'.

Thirdly, each caring moment helps us to appreciate that we should think of organisations as 'social worlds' (Bate, 1994). In other words, the organisation for and within which we work is a (Bate, 1994, p. 15):

social rather than a physical entity, made up of people talking, acting, interacting and transacting with other people. Hence the idea that culture exists not so much 'inside' or 'outside' people as 'between' people.

Finally, each caring moment serves to remind us that we need to think of the clinical workplace and organisation as a 'constructed' world. It is something made, something fashioned. Here I am arguing that what, among other things, are constructed are stories that speak about healthcare issues, problems, successes, heroes /heroines and villains, and past, present and future actions.

9. Building worlds and selves

This collection of caring moments represents a study of discourse, in this instance healthcare discourse. It characterises discourse generally as the study of the talk and texts of social life (Stevens, 1996). Thinking about discourse in this way helps us to appreciate that through language and writing we not only 'construct' the world but also ourselves within it. Writing each caring moment has been a demanding business. It has required that the writers be conscious of how they have constructed their 'stories' and the values that have led to the particular perspective chosen. In reflecting on each caring moment they have had to be accountable for how and what they claim to know. At this point we should be mindful of the Brunerian view, namely that there is not just one 'right' way of constructing meaning and reality (Bruner, 1990, 1993). We understand and build worlds for ourselves wearing certain lenses, with certain purposes in mind and interests to serve. Caring moments are complex stories about aspects of healthcare. Perhaps we should remember that the more complex and potentially unintelligible that people's lived experiences are, the greater the need for and significance of 'moments', as depicted in this book, become as ways of making experience meaningful (Boje and Dennehy, 1993).

10. Caring about others and caring for ourselves

Each caring moment is a consideration of care, expressed in different ways and occurring in different settings. They demonstrate care for others. They also reflect how certain caring values are lived out in practice and how these might be tied together into some kind of personal bundle of caring behaviours that says something important about the healthcare professional(s) and the 'subject(s)' involved (e.g. clients, students). One of the many things we can learn from these caring moments is how expansive and multi-layered the concept of care actually is. The reconstruction of the 'moment' and the writer's reflections on it emphasise this point. Caring, as depicted in each 'moment', is clearly experiential and participatory. By this I mean grounded in relationships and actions. Safe and accountable practice and quality 'service delivery', governed by the ethics of caring illustrated in this book, should arguably view respectful and meaningful relationships as both means and a goal. Thus we learn from the contents of this book that caring might usefully be appreciated as being about interactions between individuals, commitment, trust, reciprocity, participation, and a concern for and acceptance of the other.

Conclusion

At the start of this chapter I suggested that this book might be seen as a book of powerful stories of caring. In many ways I feel that they reflect something of the essence of healthcare (Kitson, 1999) because of their focus on personhood and patient-centred care. Each moment has a history and a future. It comes from somewhere and goes somewhere. The moments are not frozen but 'dynamic texts'. In this sense they illustrate some of the fundamental components of 'caring'. Arguably these are: an intention to act, actions, justifications and consequences.

I have said before that working with experience is a central feature of reflective practices. Experience is a private thing. To make it public we have to find some means of representing it. Here, caring moments are the means. Once public, our experiences or caring moments, can be reflected upon in different ways. They can be thought about again, edited, interrogated, explored, revised and shared. Our healthcare experiences can never be displayed in their original form. They have to be represented in some way. Learning from experience, through reflection, therefore involves an important act of representation. The meaning we derive from these is constrained by the form of representation chosen. We cannot say everything in one form. Perhaps healthcare professionals need the courage to 'tell' using different forms of representation? In poetic, visual, musical, still and video forms, 3D modelling, concept mapping, as well as narrative forms for example? I appreciate that this may well be asking some to do what they feel they cannot do. But the point I am trying to emphasise is that each representation only makes a certain amount of understanding possible. It does not tell us everything. Each one only reveals aspects of care. Perhaps what we need to be clearer about is the relevance and appropriateness of the different forms of representation in helping us move thinking and healthcare practice forward. Representing and understanding each caring moment therefore invite a level of invention and interpretation. I suggest that these 'moments' also invite a level of commitment: a commitment to reflect on care. Reflection *is* something to be reaffirmed continually in everyday practice.

References

Bate, P. (1994) *Strategies for Cultural Change*. Butterworth-Heinemann, Oxford.

Boje, D. and Dennehy, R. (1993) *Managing in the Postmodern World: America's Revolution against Exploitation*. Kendall-Hunt, Dubuque, IA.

Boud, D., Keogh, R. and Walker, D. (eds.) (1998) *Reflection: Turning Experience into Learning*. Kogan Page, London.

Bowles, N. (1995) Storytelling: a search for meaning within nursing practice. *Nurse Education Today*, **15**, 365–9.

Bruner, J. (1990) *Acts of Meaning*. Harvard University Press, Cambridge, MA.

Bruner, J. (1993) The autobiographical process. In: *The Culture of Autobiography* (ed. R. Folkenflik). Stanford University Press, Stanford, CA.

Day, C. (1999) Researching teaching through reflective practice. In: *Researching Teaching: Methodologies and Practices for Understanding Pedagogy* (ed. J. Loughran). Falmer Press, London.

Driscoll, J. (1999a) Getting the most from clinical supervision: Part one, the supervisee. *Mental Health Practice*, **2**(6), 28–35.

Driscoll, J. (1999b) Getting the most from clinical supervision: Part two, the supervisor. *Mental Health Practice*, **3**(1), 31–7.

Driscoll, J. (2000) *Practising Clinical Supervision: A Reflective Approach*, Ch. 6 and 7. Baillière Tindall (in association with the RCN), London.

Fine, M. and Weis, L. (1998) Writing the 'wrongs' of fieldwork: confronting our own research/writing dilemmas in urban ethnographies. In: *Being Reflexive in Critical Educational and Social Research* (eds. G. Shacklock and J. Smyth). Falmer Press, London.

Freire, P. and Faundez, A. (1989) *Learning to Question: A Pedagogy of Liberation*. WCC Publications, Geneva.

Ghaye, T. and Ghaye, K. (1998) *Teaching and Learning through Critical Reflective Practice*. David Fulton Publishers, London.

Ghaye, T. and Lillyman, S. (2010) *Reflection: Principles and Practice for Healthcare Professionals*, 2nd edn. Quay Books, London.

Ghaye, T., Cuthberth, S. and Danai, K. (1996) *Theory-Practice Relationships: Reconstructing Practice, Self-supported Learning Experiences for Healthcare Professionals*. Pentaxion Press, Newcastle-upon-Tyne.

Ghaye, T., Gillespie, D. and Lillyman, S. (eds.) (2000) *Empowerment Through Reflection: The Narratives of Healthcare Professionals*. Quay Books, London.

Harre, R. (1998) *The Singular Self: An Introduction to the Psychology of Parenthood*. Sage Publications, London.

Johns, C. and Freshwater, D. (eds.) (1998) *Transforming Nursing through Reflective Practice*. Blackwell Science, Oxford.

Kitson, A. (1999) The essence of nursing. *Nursing Standard*, **13**(23), 42–6.

Schafer, R. (1992) *Retelling a Life: Narration and Dialogue in Psychoanalysis*. Basic Books, New York.

Schon, D. (1983) *The Reflective Practitioner*. Basic Books, New York.

Stevens, R. (ed.) (1996) *Understanding the Self*. Sage Publications, London.

Thompson, J. (1997) *Lead with Vision: Manage the Strategic Challenge*. Thompson Business Press, London.

Tripp, D. (1998) Critical incidents in action inquiry. In: *Being Reflexive in Critical Educational and Social Research* (eds. G. Shacklock and J. Smyth). Falmer Press, London.

Usher, R. (1998) The story of the self: education, experience and autobiography. In: *Biography and Education: A Reader* (ed. M. Erben). Falmer Press, London.

Vezeau, T. (1993) Storytelling: a practitioner's tool. *American Journal of Maternal/Child Nursing*, **18**, 193–6.

Wallemaq, A. and Sims, D. (1998) The struggle with sense. In: *Discourse* and *Organisation* (eds. D. Grant, T. Keenoy and C. Oswick). Sage Publications, London.

CHAPTER 3

Making sense of practice through reflection: the use of critical incidents

Sue Lillyman

Throughout this book you will find practitioners' accounts of experiences which they have identified as caring moments. In this chapter I will identify how a critical incident, within a healthcare setting, can be used to identify some of the qualities of a caring moment and how it can assist the practitioner in developing their clinical practice.

What is a critical incident?

Critical incidents can take many forms. They provide the practitioner with an account of a personal experience through which they can identify how they develop and justify their practice. Ghaye and Lillyman (2006, p. 65) describe an incident as an experience that can be:

- an incident that is an ordinary experience
- an incident where the experience did not go to plan (this may be a positive as well as a negative experience)
- an incident that went well
- an incident that reflects the values and beliefs held by the individual
- an incident that identifies the contribution of qualified practitioners
- an incident that allows the identification of learning

The incident relates to an experience which the practitioner has encountered during his or her practice. This incident is then recorded, reflected upon and analysed in order to develop, enhance or justify the practitioner's contribution to patient/client care.

There are many definitions of critical incidents, however, Tripp (1993, p. 8) sums it up when he states:

Incidents happen, but critical incidents are produced by the way we look at a situation, it is an interpretation of the significance of the event.

For nurses and healthcare workers the words 'critical' and 'incident' both have different meanings from those described by Tripp. 'Critical' often refers to the state or condition of a patient or situation that is used in a negative or traumatic context within nursing. It also suggests an area of advanced specialist care, such as 'critical care units'.

The word 'incident' also implies negative aspects of care. It is currently used in nursing when some major or significant event has occurred that may require at a later date some confirmation in a legal sense. An 'incident form' is then completed. For the purpose of this book the 'critical incident' is not identified as a negative aspect of care. I view critical incidents as experiences that have had some impact on our practice. The incident may appear trivial to other practitioners and appear unworthy of any reflection or analysis to others. The point is that everyday events provide practitioners with potential learning situations and it is these that become our critical incidents.

These incidents could be referred to as experiences that had some form of emotional impact on the practitioner and are sometimes referred to as 'learning experiences' to remove the negative connotations of the title critical incident. According to Love (1996), for the event to be a critical incident it should evoke deep thought and raise a professional issue. These aspects of critical incidents are clearly demonstrated throughout this book where practitioners have encountered an experience that has affected their practice and has usually raised some emotional feelings. Rich and Parker (1995) suggest that without any structure of reflection, of an associated critical incident, analysis may potentially lead to disaffection. For this reason I advocate a structured approach to analysis as identified in Ghaye and Lillyman (2006). Critical incidents, following reflection and analysis, allow the individual to identify learning from their experiences in relation to identifying new practice, the way theory interacts with clinical work and/or justifying their practice. Parker *et al.* (1995) suggest that this process may be viewed as synonymous with meaningful discovery. They suggest that learning from experience always begins with reflection-on-practice and an analysis and evaluation of it. It is the latter that provides the practitioner with the evidence to move practice forward.

The value of critical incidents

For some, learning through critical incidents has been used to bridge any perceived gaps between theory and practice (Parker *et al.*, 1995; Chesney, 1996). Critical incidents may also be regarded as a valuable framework for promoting reflective practice (Minghella and Benson, 1995). According to Smith and Russell (1991) they assist the practitioner in looking at a situation from multiple perspectives and heighten awareness of the complex skills within nursing. Reflecting on critical incidents is concerned with providing quality care to our patients/clients. Norman *et al.* (1992) used the critical incident technique to identify perceptions of quality nursing care. This, I suggest, is an aspect the individual can use for his or her own practice and in relation to clinical governance (Department of Health, 1997).

In the current climate of healthcare, nursing practitioners, as well as other health professionals, are required, through their various *Codes of Conduct* (e.g. Nursing and Midwifery Council, 2008), to demonstrate their clinical competence. Critical incident analysis is a process that can be used by the reflective practitioner for this purpose. This process, together with the notion of clinical governance, relies on self-audit by practitioners to demonstrate their levels of competency in practice. Saylor (1990) suggests that the ability to reflect upon one's practice is essentially for competency and therefore advocates the use of critical incidents for this purpose. Burnard (1990) argues that learning from experience, if used effectively, can have a direct and indirect effect on improving the quality of nursing education, management and care. Arguably, this is the aim not only of the individual practitioner, but is also high on political and professional agendas.

Critical incidents are also identified by Schon (1983) as a valuable learning process. Smith and Russell (1991) argue that through the process of reflection-on-action an effective practitioner will be produced, able to define and redefine problems within practice. The critical incident then within this context is a valuable focus for learning.

In this book critical incidents of various kinds have been used to identify 'caring moments' within healthcare provision settings. In another book in this series, Ghaye and Lillyman (2007) which overtly links reflection with clinical supervision, practitioners have reflected upon the supervision session in order to identify and develop specific practice within a caring role. These too can be identified as 'caring moments' within practice. In Ghaye *et al.* (2000) critical incidents are used in another form to identify how reflection can lead to the empowering of colleagues and clients. The incident is therefore the catalyst for reflection and the focus for helping to transform practice. Without analysis and reflection, using critical incidents becomes an exercise in describing practice and does not allow the practitioner to gain any significantly new insights or development from the event.

It is therefore the analysis that leads practitioners on to develop and enhance practice, decision-making or broaden their knowledge base. As already identified, this requires a structured and supported process to guide the individual through. We can see different approaches throughout this book where an identified model is used for reflection. For example, Chapter 8 uses Gibbs' (1988) model as a process for structured reflection. Each stage of his cycle is identified as the individual practitioner addresses the provision of care for a patient within the endoscopy unit. This approach allows the practitioner to identify a limitation in his or her own knowledge base and a change within the unit policy relating to new staff. Chapter 9 uses another approach to analysis, where Tripp's (1993) 'thinking strategy' is used to make more sense of a critical incident. There are many models of reflection in the healthcare literature. Each model invites the practitioner to think again about practice in a certain way. They all have the potential to enlighten. They all have limitations as well. A range of models are reviewed and critiqued in Ghaye and Lillyman (2006). In this book the range of models reviewed are finally grouped and labelled thus:

- *Structured models*: Johns (1994)
- *Hierarchical models*: Mezirow (1981), Van Manen (1977) and Goodman (1984)
- *Iterative models*: Kolb (1984), Gibbs (1988), Atkins and Murphy (1994) and Boud *et al* (1985)
- *Synthetic models*: Louden (1991)
- *Holistic models*: Ghaye *et al* (1996)

The model used for reflection should be the choice of the practitioner. The type of incident or caring moment they are trying to come to know better and more richly may affect the choice of model.

Caring moments

Some of the caring moments described in this book relate to critical incidents that practitioners have encountered as part of their everyday work. They are often then analysed using some form of structured approach/model of reflection such as those of Gibbs (1988), Johns (1994) or Kolb (1984). These incidents all relate to what the authors have identified as 'caring moments'. They are incidents that have left an impression on the practitioner, such as the patient being given bad news or the group of students who demonstrated their own reflective skills within the learning environment, and provided the practitioner with an incident that they can record and reflect upon in relation to improving their own practice. Through the analysis of and reflection on these caring moments practice is firmly linked to theory and issues are identified through some form of emotional response to a situation. Ultimately, through reflection, care may well be improved, with the practitioner being able to demonstrate their own competence within their area of expertise. Norman *et al.* (1992) noted that the appropriate basic unit of analysis was not the incident itself but the happenings revealed by incidents that are critical by virtue of being important to respondents with respect to the quality of nursing care. Therefore, to stop at identifying an incident or caring moment, the descriptive phase of the process, will not be valuable to either the practitioner or the profession.

One limitation in relation to critical incidents, noted by Smith and Russell (1991), is that the retrospective evaluation of personal experience can be subject to subconscious editing. This may provide the espoused theory being identified rather than the theory-in-practice. For this reason we recommend the use of learning journals in which to record the critical incidents as they occur. This will then provide practitioners with a more accurate picture of what happened before they start to put their own interpretations on the event with the fading memory.

We note that some reflection takes place within the recording of the incident; however, this is the first stage of the process. The whole issue in using the critical incident analysis framework is to make the point that caring moments can be reflected upon and learned from in this way. It is one of a number of approaches to reflection that can help to move thinking and practice forward in a justified manner. Smith and Russell (1991) note that clinical knowledge develops as practical experiences are combined with the application of theoretical knowledge, with this being further redefined and extended within practice. The whole process is cyclical, integrating theory and practice. Rosenal (1995) notes that the process of using critical incidents can guide the learner/practitioner through a process with which they may be unfamiliar, thereby enhancing practice through experiential learning.

One view of a caring moment then can be summed up as an experience that the individual has encountered with patients, clients, colleagues and/or students that has had a significant effect on the individual and provided the basis for a learning experience on which the individual can, or perhaps should, reflect. Each caring moment throughout the book relates to either direct care or educational provision, leading to improved care through a specific incident. Critical incidents are a particular way of both naming and understanding care. It is a process of moving practice forward and can be used as evidence of self-development within practice and as part of the individual's personal professional profile. Identifying these caring moments as aspects of practice that need to be thought about again is even more pertinent as nursing, midwifery and health visiting become more accountable through the process of clinical governance (Department of Health, 1997). Critical incident analysis is one of a number of approaches that can be utilised by each practitioner in the pursuit of safe and accountable practice.

References

Atkins, S. and Murphy, K. (1994) Reflective practice. *Nursing Standard*, **8**(39), 49–56.

Boud, D., Keogh, R. and Walker, D. (1985) Promoting reflection in learning: a model. In: *Reflection: Turning Experience into Learning* (eds. D. Boud, R. Keogh and D. Walker). Kogan Page, New York.

Burnard, P. (1990) Group discussion. *Nursing Times*, **86**(37), 36–7.

Chesney, M. (1996) (1996) Sharing reflections on critical incidents in midwifery practice. *British Journal of Midwifery*, **4**(1), 8–10.

Department of Health (1997) *The New NHS: Modern and Dependable*. HMSO, London

Ghaye, T. and Lillyman, S. (2006) *Learning Journals and Critical Incidents: Reflective Practice for Health Care Professionals*, 2nd edn. Quay Books, London.

Ghaye, T. and Lillyman, S. (eds.) (2007) *The Role of Reflection in Effective Clinical Supervision*, 2nd edn. Quay Books, London.

Ghaye, T. *et al.* (1996) *Learning Through Critical Reflective Practice: Self-Supported Learning Experiences for Health Care Professionals*. Pentaxion, Newcastle-upon-Tyne.

Ghaye, T., Gillespie, D. and Lillyman, S. (eds.) (2000) *Empowerment Through Reflection: The Narratives of Health Care Professionals*. Quay Books, London.

Gibbs, G. (1988) *Learning by Doing: A Guide to Teaching and Learning Methods*. Further Education Unit, Oxford Brookes University, Oxford.

Goodman, J. (1984) Reflection in teacher education: a case study and theoretical analysis. *Interchange*, **15**(3), 9–26.

Johns, C. (1994) Nuances of reflection. *Journal of Clinical Nursing*, **3**, 71–5.

Kolb, D. (1984) *Experiential Learning Experience as the Source of Learning and Development*. Prentice Hall, New Jersey.

Louden, W. (1991) *Understanding Teaching*. Cassell, London.

Love, C. (1996) Critical Incidents and PREP. *Professional Nurse*, **11**(9), 574–577.

Mezirow, J. (1981) A critical theory of adult learning and education. *Adult Education*, **32**(1), 3–24.

Minghella, E. and Benson, A. (1995) Developing reflective practice in mental health nursing through critical incident analysis. *Journal of Advanced Nursing*, **21**, 205–13.

Norman, I., Redfern, S., Tomalin, D. and Oliver, S. (1992) Developing Flanagan's critical incident technique to elicit indicators of high and low quality nursing care for patients and their nurses. *Journal of Advanced Nursing*, **17**, 590–600.

Nursing and Midwifery Council (2008) *The Code: Standards of Conduct, Performance and Ethics for Nurses and Midwives*. NMC, London.

Parker, D., Webb, D. and D'Souza, B. (1995) The value of critical incident analysis as an educational tool and its relationship to experiential learning. *Nurse Education Today*, **15**, 111–16.

Rich, A. and Parker, D. (1995) Reflection and critical incident analysis: ethical and moral implications of their use within nursing and midwifery education. *Journal of Advanced Nursing*, **22**, 1050–7.

Rosenal, L. (1995) Exploring the learner's world: critical incident methodology. *Journal of Continuing Education in Nursing*, **26**(3), 115–18.

Saylor, C. (1990) Reflection and professional education: art and science and competency. *Nurse Educator*, **15**(2), 8–11.

Schon, D. (1983) *The Reflective Practitioner*. Temple Smith, London.

Smith, A. and Russell, J. (1991) Using critical learning incidents in nurse education. *Nurse Education Today*, **11**, 284–91.

Tripp, D. (1993) *Critical Incidents in Teaching*. Routledge, London.

Van Manen, D. (1977) Linking ways of knowing with ways of being practical. *Curriculum Enquiry*, **6**(3), 205–28.

CHAPTER 4

What if caring is not enough? The importance of positivity

Tony Ghaye

The context

In the UK there is a rapidly evolving political and health policy environment. The developments outlined in the UK coalition government's 2010 White Paper *Equity and Excellence: Liberating the NHS* (Department of Health, 2010) are radical and far-reaching, and include, for example, fundamental changes to the role of general practice. The devolution of commissioning to general practice consortia will require a more transparent and systematic approach to how the quality of care in general practice is monitored, managed and reported. This will go well beyond the existing Quality Outcomes Framework (QOF) and current patient experience surveys. In this evolving context, the title of this book, *When Caring is Not Enough* becomes pertinent and provocative. The aim of this chapter is to explore this and to make a number of suggestions.

Introduction

I was facilitating a multi-professional discussion recently about ways to improve the quality of care in general practice in the UK. It was an important event, given the recent King's Fund publication, which stated (Kings Fund, 2011, p. xi):

> For many in general practice, it (improving general practice) is not an area of health care greatly given to self-reflection and self-challenge. One of our hopes is that this inquiry will bring home the importance of greater self-examination.

There was a long debate about defining and measuring quality. This perhaps was not surprising given the radical overhaul of the ways in which the NHS is being reorganised and required to deliver its services. GPs will have a key role to play in the reformed NHS, as commissioners as well as providers of care. An important implication of this is that general practice will become increasingly involved in, and responsible for, the health of local populations. It is also not surprising because it is important to answer the question, 'What does quality mean?'. It is complex and multi-faceted. There was much discussion about the quality of care with regard to diagnosis, referral, prescribing and health promotion.

When the conversation shifted to the non-clinical aspects of general practice, care was discussed mainly in terms of access to care, the continuity of care and the need to try to engage positively with patients in order to understand their views on the quality of care they felt they received. The discussion really ignited when we got on to the underlying context in which care was being managed and delivered – in other words, the *environment* in which quality care, and improvements in care, can best be promoted, supported and sustained. The discussion was reformulated into a question, namely, 'How can practices be supported so that they can create an environment within which the quality of care can be continuously improved and can flourish?'. At one point in this discussion a practice manager said:

> It's clear to me that we have to get back to some basic issues. How we are going to relate to our patients. How we can best meet their needs. How much time we can give them. What consequences our care will have. Simply caring, or wanting to care well for our patients, may not be enough. All these new developments are putting us under more and more pressure. We are no longer 'gatekeepers' to specialist care but more like 'navigators'. We need to think about skill-mix and team working. We may have to think about ourselves more. We may have to consider the question, 'Is caring enough?' and 'If we can't care for ourselves, first, how on earth can we be expected to care for others?'

That one statement opened the door for a significant moment where stories were shared about 'caring'. These short stories revealed much about the individuals' assumptions, beliefs, habits and relationships with their patients. They embraced *eudaimonistic* questions like, 'What is good care?', 'On what grounds do I make decisions?' and 'How do I decide what to do that is in the patient's best interests?'. It became clear that telling stories was certainly not a waste of precious time, but integral to the development of professional knowledge. With appropriate levels of trust and appreciation, stories can be a way to interrogate and to disrupt 'practice as usual'. There was a common thread to all the stories. They often centred on a desire to 'make a positive difference' to the lives of patients. Put another way, these were stories of altruism. Altruism can be a source of intense pleasure. For some it is a virtue. I suggest that recent political and policy developments in healthcare in the UK serve to problematise and to challenge altruism. The goodness of this value is being called into question. Could altruism, defined as the appropriate commissioning and provision of care that makes a positive difference to the lives of patients, be a problem? Caring, just because it is generally considered to be *good*, may not be enough. The new healthcare context may be suggesting that it is time to consider other *goods*. In this chapter I suggest another *good*. It is about experiencing, developing and using positive emotions productively at work. I shall refer this as *positivity*.

The brave new world of work

The political and policy developments I outlined above have a number of potential consequences for the ways in which healthcare professionals are encouraged, and are supported, to care for their patients. Clearly what is important here are the connections between contemporary (and future) work practices (and the management of them), and the health and well-being of those healthcare professionals, who work (often longer, harder and with less security) and are still pursuing the quest for continuous care improvement. And then there is the idea of work life balance to think about (Department of Trade and Industry, 2003). In this context, what are the implications for wanting to care? What happens if this desire is not enough? What impact could this have on those who (still) wish to be regarded as professional, resilient, effective and so on? How do we care in a context that Bauman (2001) describes as being 'saturated with uncertainty'? Arguably the new world of healthcare work, proposed by the UK coalition government, is encouraging all healthcare professionals to know themselves: to (re)consider their values and how these are put into practice. This is no bad thing. But it requires quite a sophisticated grasp of learning through reflection. Reflection is critical at times when services are changing at warp speed and where performing consistently at high levels and in an ethical way is seemingly more difficult, but more necessary, than ever. Reflection is therefore a necessity, not a luxury.

I suggest that one important consequence of all of this is the need to rethink what we mean by professional development. It seems that we cannot afford simply to continue to address (only) the knowledge and skills of healthcare professionals, thus developing their cognitive capacities. We need to consider their emotional well-being. This crucially involves how healthcare workers renew and recover energy as much as how they use it. It depends as much on how they manage their lives and their work. When people feel strong and resilient, physically, mentally, emotionally and spiritually, they perform better, with more passion, for longer

(Groppel, 2000; Loehr and Schwartz, 2001, 2003; Kang, 2006). When morale is low and our ability to be resilient is taking a bashing, passion and performance suffer. Like losing weight or ending an addiction, anything that requires us to change, not only our attention, but also our attitude and practices, is hard work. This is why I am suggesting that caring (alone) may not be enough. Positivity matters, and two crucial aspects of this are morale and resilience. Morale is a quality that enables staff to pull together, and to stay well and positive when times are tough. When morale is high staff are more able to stay focused on their work and to be committed to it (Robertsoncooper, 2010). So this is about staff engagement – full engagement (Loehr and Schwartz, 2003). Fostering this is important in healthcare now. Resilience is about people's ability to stay positive even when the going gets tough. It is about being able to cope well and to think clearly under pressure. Morale and resilience are mutually supportive. They contribute (with others things) to our general feeling of positivity.

Enhancing positivity – the case of a child development centre

A colleague of mine, Karen Deeny, worked extensively with centre team members who were employed by an NHS Trust. They worked together in a dedicated single-storey building located in the community between a hospital and a school. The team was recognised within the local community as a source of expertise and support for children with special needs and their families. The team comprised people with a range of job roles, including specialist nurses and nursery nurses, a speech and language therapist, physiotherapist, occupational therapist, play therapist, nursery assistants, clerical and administrative staff, paediatricians and volunteers. The team was made up of what had previously been two separate NHS teams that had been merged six months prior to Karen starting work with them. The merger was generally described by staff as an uncomfortable and unwelcome experience, although they recognised that it was important for them to find ways of working together in the future. Now acting in the role of change facilitator for the Trust, Karen was familiar with the team, having been a speech and language therapist at the centre for five years. The challenge for Karen was to enable all at the centre to merge their services in a constructive way. This required a sense of positivity, the building of morale and some resilience.

Karen kept a detailed reflective diary of her experiences. Extracts from her diary were included in her work called 'Discovering ways of working appreciatively with healthcare teams to enable them to look at and learn from their practice' (Deeny, 2010). What follows is an extract from Deeny (2010). It vividly illustrates that caring is not enough!

Extract from Karen's reflective diary

Although the team talked about their motivation to find ways of working more constructively together, they repeatedly referred to the '*baggage*' from their past working relationships that they felt was impacting on their attempts to move forwards. I sensed some frustration, illustrated by the team members' comments below, that although they were investing in time together, they were not moving towards improving their team working in the way they hoped and that progress was slow.

- I feel we don't approach what we do as a whole team. Some people consider themselves to be separate. I'd like us to be united but worry that unless we all agree to change we will remain fragmented. We should be able to agree the same goals.
- How do you build a team when services have been put together, but have different rules? There is a sense of them and us. I would like for us to be one team working and giving our best to all groups.
- I think some issues have been not addressed for some people in the group and until these are addressed they cannot cross 'the bridge' and feel part of a team.
- I feel we all need to keep together for the issues to be explored and to enable staff to move forward together, and enjoy a better working relationship with each other.
- I am fed up with all the baggage. We need a positive way forward and especially total honesty between all is a must for us to move forward and build on our strengths.
- Just as we begin to communicate at a meaningful level, someone seems to get hurt, we need to find a way of communicating.

To help me consider how I might plan future sessions in order to create better opportunities for improved team working I wrote down the following reflective notes at the time:

I wonder whether the activities and conversations with the team so far have not been 'different' enough and as a result have simply precipitated negative interactions similar to the ones that have prevailed in the past. The team seem to 'get stuck' in talking about problems and seem unable to identify what might make a difference for them and might enable them to improve their team working. They seem to be 'stuck in the problem.' (February 2004).

My reflective notes helped me identify two main themes – firstly, that I needed **to do** something that was going to strongly emphasise the appreciative over the critical. It seemed that 'reflecting on the problem' was sustaining the problem itself and was not helping the team move towards a solution. Secondly, I felt I needed **to do** something different in order to give the team 'permission' to create an atmosphere to foster a different kind of conversation and that might enable more voices and views to contribute to the 'strategising' in identifying ways forward for the team.

I decided to address this directly in our next session together. I was concerned to plan the words I would use to open the session carefully so as to set the scene for something different. Below are the words I prepared and closely followed to open the session:

'I am going to suggest that we try out something a bit different today in order to try to move forward with your wish to work more effectively together. We have spoken a lot about how communication issues seem to be a continuing concern for you. We know these are not new issues and have been around for quite some time. There seems to be a pattern here about talking about problems and focusing on the problem rather than thinking about possible solutions. I am going to suggest that doing something differently in this session might help to change the patterns of conversation and to help us work out some possible ways forward to a more positive sense of team working.' (April 2004).

Inspired by the comment from a team member about 'crossing the bridge', I wrote the words 'communication issues' and 'improved team working' on two large pieces of paper and placed them on the floor, in the middle of the circle of staff as reminders of what we were focusing on. I then invited each team member to take a large marker pen and a large piece of sugar paper, presented in a range of colours and shapes, and to write their own suggestion for one thing they felt could make a difference in moving from a state of 'communication issues' to one of 'improved team working'. Each team member then placed their piece of paper on the floor in the middle of the circle and we removed the chairs so that everyone could walk around and see what everyone had written. The team were then invited to rearrange the sugar paper shapes using their suggestions for 'one thing that could make a difference' to build an 'activities bridge' (see Figure 4.1) between the two 'ends' marked 'communication issues' and 'improved team working'.

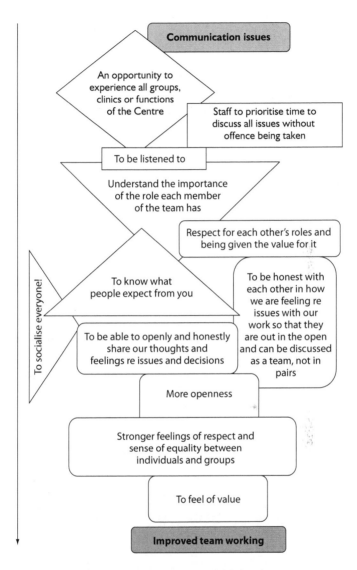

Figure 4.1 Enhancing positivity in a child development centre.

Moving from deficits to strengths

What this case study shows is that caring for children (alone) is not enough. In this context of a merger of services, something in addition to caring is required. It is what I am calling *positivity*. I am suggesting that to help health and social care staff become the best they can be, we need to reflect on real positives (hard to find though they may be in certain circumstances) and use reflection and its practices to identify, develop and amplify team members' gifts, talents and strengths. This is a point about balance. I am not advocating replacing the one-sided perspective of reflection being a solution looking for a problem (an obsession with what is wrong), with another one-sided perspective (an exclusive focus on what is right). This is misguided and simplistic. I am trying to go beyond this swinging pendulum kind of reflective practice by advocating an approach to individual growth and performance that recognises that both strengths and weaknesses have an appropriate place in learning and professional development.

But here is a key personal question. What do you think will help you be most successful in your work and get most fulfilment from it? Building your strengths or fixing your weaknesses? Maybe it's a bit of both? If you gave these choices to a colleague, what do you think they'd say? If they work in a target-driven, high performance-oriented, externally assessed and inspected organisation like an NHS Trust, where resources are becoming scarcer, and personal and external accountability stronger, I think I know what they'd naturally (and some may argue, understandably) say: fix our weaknesses. In other words, we use reflective practices to get rid of the things we don't do well and hopefully things will get better. We invest what precious time we may have, reflecting (maybe together rather than alone) on what we want to 'fix' and remove rather than what we want to have more of and to amplify. Is this wise?

A focus on reflection for strength-building takes us into some new, interesting and humanly significant areas, such as those to do with excellence, creativity, resilience and optimal functioning (Ghaye, 2011). When people are performing in roles in which they play to their strengths, studies show that performance and satisfaction increase, productivity improves and they have a greater chance of achieving their full potential (Buckingham and Clifton, 2001). This is a radical departure from the long-held view that to enable someone to perform at his or her best you work as hard as you can at trying to overcome their weaknesses. This view is evidenced by the fact that only 20% of employees in companies across the globe feel that their strengths are in play on a daily basis (Buckingham and Clifton, 2001). So my argument here is that it is a great investment in time and other resources to use reflective practices to develop strengths and to build workplaces where these strengths can be used for the majority of our time, each day.

Staying positive – caring well

If you feel caring is not enough in the current healthcare context, you may need to check out your level of positivity towards your work, your colleagues, patients and organisation. Positivity comes in many flavours. It can also be fragile. It is possible for you to experience it. But it depends on how you think. Like all emotions, positive ones arise from the way in which you interpret ideas, actions and events as they unfold. How far are you aware that you have the power to turn positivity on and off for yourself?

- Try this. Turn positivity **ON** right now. Ask yourself:
  - What's right about my current circumstances?
  - What makes me lucky to be here?
  - What aspect of my current circumstances is a gift to be treasured?
- Now turn positivity **OFF**. Ask yourself these positivity-spoiling questions:
  - What's wrong here, right now?
  - Why do I feel so fed up?
  - Who can I blame for this?

The broaden-and-build theory

I suggest that Fredrickson's (2001) broaden-and-build theory is a very useful 'thinking framework' for us, especially in times of rapid change. Her theory describes the form and function of a number of positive emotions, including joy, interest, contentment and love. A key proposition is that these positive emotions broaden an individual's momentary thought-action repertoire. This means that when we feel positive, we are generally more open-minded, more receptive to new ideas, more adaptive and more flexible. For example, joy sparks the urge to play, interest sparks the urge to explore, contentment sparks the urge to savour and love sparks a recurring cycle of each of these urges within safe, close relationships. The broadened mindsets arising from these positive emotions are contrasted with the narrowed mindsets sparked by many negative emotions (specific action tendencies, such as to attack or flee). In other words when we feel more negative we feel much less prepared and able to consider alternatives, to 'play' with ideas and to consider options.

A second key proposition of this theory concerns the consequences of these broadened mindsets. By broadening an individual's momentary thought-action repertoire, whether through play, exploration or similar activities, positive emotions promote discovery of novel and creative actions, ideas and social bonds, which in turn build that individual's personal resources and ability to be

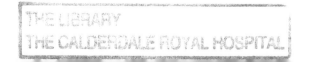

resilient. These can range from physical and intellectual resources, to social and psychological ones. Importantly, these resources function as reserves that can be drawn on later to improve the prospect of successful coping, survival and good health. There is an important knock-on effect going on here. As positivity grows, so does our ability to be more open-minded and wholehearted in what we do. With this positive mindset comes a greater ability to actually try things out, to experiment and to improve what we do. Fredrickson (2009) argues that we can actually work at increasing our sense of positivity and that it also:

- Makes us feel good
- Changes how our mind works
- Can transform our future
- Puts the brakes on negativity

More specifically, Fredrickson (2004, p. 1367) argues that:

... positive emotions signal optimal functioning, but this is far from their whole story... positive emotions also produce optimal functioning, not just within the present, pleasant moment, but over the long term as well. The bottom-line message is that people should cultivate positive emotions in themselves and in those around them.

Reflection-for-resilience

Resilience is a strength. It can be developed. It is linked to you how positive you feel. So it is worth reflecting upon. At work you may have noticed that some colleagues are simply less fazed by setbacks than others, clearly showing more resilience, whatever life throws at them. People like this are able to learn from their experience, be adaptable and flexible according to the demands of their work environment, and are energised rather than drained by crises and problems; other people actively choose to collaborate with them (Clarke and Nicholson, 2010). Some people are more resilient than others, but why? Why do some people seem better able to bounce back from whatever life throws at them than others? We know that individuals respond differently to different events. So what's the key? Some people seem more able to exploit the positive events in their life. Some are proactive problem-solvers. Some have a tendency to tackle issues rather than avoid them. Some people seem to have a radar system that provides them with information about the need to change. Some seem able to keep things in perspective and see beyond the immediate pressures of their everyday working life. And crucially some know where to look for assistance. Arguably these are some of the characteristics of resilient people. Reflection that promotes positivity can play an important role in building resilience. This may be crucial in times when caring is not enough. One way to think about resilience is to think of it as the ability not to see failure, or failing, as something to dwell on, but as an opportunity to learn from and to move forward, accepting that failure is a part of life. If this sounds a bit negative, here is another view. It could be argued that resilience is based on two things: (a) a belief in and commitment to what you're doing, and (b) confidence that you can make things better. There are at least four implications of taking this view. I suggest they are:

- Being comfortable with who you are
- Being clear about your values
- Having other interests which provides a source of relief, even escape, and that help you get a sense of perspective on things
- Having drive, determination, matched with realistic optimism. In life and work we can't win all the battles!

What if caring is not enough? The importance of positivity

Caring for your patients and working with your colleagues in the best way you can, I suggest, requires you to reflect on your levels of positivity and how this effects your practice. A practical way to begin to think about developing and enhancing your positivity is to focus on your strengths. Try to identify what they are, when you use them and how often. If you feel you do not use them enough (or even at all!) then ask yourself, 'What do I need to stop doing, *and* what do I need to start doing, so that I use my strengths more often in my work?'. Table 4.1 (overleaf) offers you a four-step process for achieving this.

Table 4.1 A four-step process for developing your positivity.

Step 1: Identify and clarify
- What do you believe are your strengths?
- What would be a 'personal best' story where you felt you played to your strengths and performed well?

Step 2: Affirming and understanding
- What do others know your strengths to be?
- What kind of alignment is there between Steps 1 and 2?

Step 3: Execute and integrate
- How far are you able to do what you do best, for the majority of your time, each day?
- What needs to change to enable you to securely integrate doing what you do best into your everyday working life?

Step 4: Amplification and impact
- How might you amplify your strengths and thereby eclipse your weaknesses?
- When you feel able to play to your strengths, what impact does this have on your level of job satisfaction, your feelings toward your colleagues and patients and sense of loyalty to your organisation?

References

Bauman, Z. (2001) *The Individualised Society*, Polity Press, Cambridge.

Buckingham, M. and Clifton, D. O. (2001) *Now, Discover Your Strengths: How to Develop Your Talents and Those of the People You Manage.* Simon & Schuster, London.

Clarke, J. and Nicholson, J. (2010) *Resilience: Bounce Back from Whatever Life Throws at You.* Crimson Publishing, Richmond.

Department of Health (2010) *Equity and Excellence: Liberating the NHS.* Department of Health, London.

Department of Trade and Industry (2003) *Work Life Balance Campaign.* http://164.36.164.20/work-lifebalance/index.html.

Deeny, K. (2010) Discovering ways of working appreciatively with healthcare teams to enable them to look at and learn from their practice, *Unpublished Doctoral Thesis*, University of Wales. Research conducted at Glyndŵr University.

Fredrickson, B. (2001) The role of positive emotions in positive psychology: the broaden-and-build theory of positive emotions. *American Psychologist*, **56**(3), 218 26.

Fredrickson, B. (2004). The broaden-and-build theory of positive emotions. *Philosophical Transactions of the Royal Society*, **359**, 1367 78.

Fredrickson, B. (2009). *Positivity: Groundbreaking Research Reveals How to Embrace the Hidden Strength of Positive Emotions, Overcome Negativity, and Thrive*. Crown Publications, New York.

Ghaye, T. (2011) *Teaching and Learning through Reflective Practice: a Practical Guide for Positive Action*, 2nd edn. Routledge, Abingdon.

Groppel, J. (2000) *The Corporate Athlete: How to Achieve Maximal Performance in Business and Life*. Wiley, Chichester.

Kang, L. (2006) *Passion at Work: How to Find Work You Love and Live the Time of Your Life*. Prentice Hall, New Jersey.

King's Fund (2011) *Improving the Quality of Care in General Practice: Report of an Independent Inquiry Commissioned by the King's Fund*. The King's Fund, London.

Loehr, J. and Schwartz, T. (2001) The making of a corporate athlete. *Harvard Business Review*, **79**(1), 120 8.

Loehr, J. and Schwartz, T. (2003) *The Power of Full Engagement – Managing Energy Not Time is the Key to High Performance and Personal Renewal*. Free Press, London.

Robertsoncooper (2010) *Building Morale and Resilience – the Key to Surviving Difficult Times*, Part 1. Robertsoncooper, Manchester.

CHAPTER 5

Difficult conversations – discussing what matters

Sue Lillyman and Heather Campbell

Introduction

Many times as healthcare professionals we are faced with difficult conversations, such as those about breaking bad news, giving a diagnosis, providing information in relation to a change in prognosis or approaching the issue of organ donation when a loved one has died. In healthcare these conversations often have implications for the person's well-being. As Gallagher (2010, p. 5) states: 'crucial conversations are difficult because no one involved wants it to happen'. They can be stressful for the patient and the healthcare professional (Barnes and Armstrong, 2010).

Some of the most difficult conversations are those when a life-limiting illness has been diagnosed, such as cancer, dementia, a chronic condition such as heart failure, chronic obstructive airways disease or motor neurone disease. The conversations that follow or need to be engaged in may have to address such issues as: how do we approach such a subject in order to discuss what matters to the person and their family? How do we answer such questions as, 'Am I dying nurse?' or 'How long have I got?'. Duhamel and Dupuis (2004) identified that nurses in particular can often feel inadequate or lack confidence to carry out these conversations, just as other healthcare professionals, such as physicians and clinicians, have difficulties (Koropchack *et al.*, 2006). However, Drew *et al.* (2001) suggest that the success of any healthcare provision depends on the quality of the interaction between the patient and healthcare professional. Therefore all healthcare professionals need to feel confident and prepared for such conversations. As Frankel and Stein (1999) note, it is the interview that can determine the outcome of care.

Various authors and researchers provide models for these conversations. For example, Frankel and Stein (1999) used what they referred to as the four habits when conducting medical interviews; McGuigan (2009) produced a ten-stage strategy for difficult conversations; and Krumberger (2003) talks about three conversations. All of these examples include the same elements and have been included within this chapter.

Difficult conversations about life-limiting conditions

In this chapter we identify how we might engage in these conversations and suggest some pointers that might help us review and engage with our patient and client and their loved ones. We use the situation in which we want to engage in a conversation about people's wishes in relation to their treatment once they are diagnosed with a life-limiting condition in relation to end of life care. In the United Kingdom we use advance statements, advance decisions to refuse treatment and/ or life-sustaining treatment, and care plans that assist the patient to identify the treatment and preferred place of death should they lose capacity during their illness to articulate their wishes.

Advance statements, decisions and care plans

Advance care decisions, advance statements and advance care plans are defined as 'a process of discussion between patient and professional carer, which sometimes includes family and friends' (Murray *et al.*, 2006, p. 868). The British Medical Association (2007, 2009) states that *advance decisions* are a clear instruction of refusing a medical procedure or intervention such as a participant in research. They note that the advance decision and refusal are made voluntarily by a competent and informed adult. These are likely to have legal force. They state that 'The purpose of an advance decision is to make provision for decisions that will need to be taken in the future after the deterioration of the individual's mental faculties' (British Medical Association, 2007, p. 3).

In these discussions the patient can make an *advance statement*, which includes positive preferences in relation to preferred place of care/death. The *advance decision* is a written document that involves informed consent for the refusal of specific treatment if a person loses capacity at any stage of their illness (Murray *et al.*, 2006). The *advance care plan* is defined by Singer *et al.* (1996, p. 1689) as 'a process whereby a patient, in consultation with healthcare providers, family members and important others, makes decisions about his or her future healthcare, should he or she become incapable of participating in medical decisions'. The British Medical Association (2009) also state that openness, dialogue and forward planning should be encouraged especially when a person has a strong belief in relation to treatment. However, through all of this nobody should feel compelled to make an advance decision, statement or care plan (British Medical Association, 2007) although the opportunity should be provided. It is in this situation that the healthcare professional might have to take the lead on initiating the conversation. As Tulsky (2005) noted, the advance care plan is a useful tool that can assist with approaching those conversations with patients about end of life. This can provide the opportunity to respond to emotions and being able to focus on goals for care rather than specific treatment.

Having the time for the conversations (90 second monologue)

One of the main concerns that many healthcare professionals have in commencing these conversations is the time factor and workload (Mauksch *et al.*, 2008; Georgaca and Avdi, 2009; McDonald *et al.*, 2010) and can, if there is a feeling that there is pressure on the time, result in low-quality, inefficient communication. Langewitz *et al.* (2002) found that from a mean time of 92 seconds of uninterrupted speech by the patient the professional could elicit relevant and informative information from the patient. A follow-up study by Rabinowitz *et al.* (2004) reported that using this 90 second monologue at the opening of the conversation helped the healthcare processional to gain more and fuller history and or elicit concerns from their patient. In Langewitz *et al.*'s (2002) study they reported that when using the 90 second monologue the patients were able to give important information, and that 80% of the patients with complex conditions found that this time was sufficient to give that initial information. Marvel *et al.* (2011) also identified that those clinicians who did not allow an uninterrupted monologue at the start of the conversation found that there were concerns that came to light later in the conversation, incomplete agenda setting and missed opportunities to gain potentially important information or the chief concern from the patient. Tapp (2001) suggested that making space for the conversations may also result in the possibility for the patient to make sense of their illness and suffering.

Commencing a difficult conversation

As stated previously, nursing and healthcare professionals often feel inadequately prepared or lack confidence in these situations (Duhamel and Dupuis, 2004; Koropchack *et al.*, 2006). Frankel and Stein (1999) identify that the professional should invest well in the beginning of the conversation if it is to be therapeutic and valuable to the patient.

As Koropchack *et al.* (2006), Uitterhoeve *et al.* (2009) and McGuigan (2009) all reported that effective communication can result in increased satisfaction with the care provided. Wright and Leahey (2000) suggest that it is the nurse's attitude that is the key element in establishing a relationship and trust at the beginning of the conversation.

Weiner and Efferent (2005) note that prior to engaging in this difficult conversation the professional should have a good pre-existing relationship with the patient, significant clinical experience and also a good recognition of the severity and chronicity of the illness the person is living with.

Some other concerns, rather than just time and workload noted above, expressed by professionals in commencing these conversations included the danger of taking away hope and that the person is not yet ready to have that conversation (Weiner and Efferent, 2005; McDonald *et al.*, 2010). However, Murray *et al.* (2006) found that even though these discussions might be uncomfortable they are more likely to engender hope, and as Detering *et al.* (2010) also found in their study that the conversations often improve end of life care and help to reduce stress anxiety and depression in the surviving relative when they know the person has had their wishes met. McGuigan (2009) also noted how the experience stays with the family.

Duhamel and Dupuis (2004) note the importance of acknowledging the need for hope. Sometimes these conversations might be serendipitous rather than planned or anticipated (Haigh, 2005) and therefore difficult to plan. However, if these are planned conversations, as part of the preparation, a period of time should be protected that can be given without interruptions, with an agreement for the conversation from the patient and that the patient is placed centrally within the conversation (McGuigan, 2009).

It should also be noted that these conversations might not necessarily all be completed in one discussion. They might be revisited over time, as people may change their mind in relation to decisions that are made early in their diagnosis and as new information in relation to their condition and treatment come to light.

Duhamel and Dupuis (2004) point out that relieving suffering and promoting hope is a real privilege for nurses and professionals, and therefore we should never underestimate the importance of this role. McGuigan (2009) highlights that healthcare professionals need to ensure that they have the appropriate skills and accurate information prior to commencing these conversations. Cues are also very important within these conversations, and Uitthoeve *et al.* (2009) identify the importance of responding to them as they are often hints of worry or concern. They note that when healthcare professionals responded to the cues appropriately they found that this was appreciated by the patient and related to patient satisfaction.

Identifying the patient's perception, concerns and agenda

Frankel and Stein (1999) identified that it is the patient's agenda that should be followed throughout the conversations. The patient's primary concern should be prioritised and adhered to in the next stage of the conversation. They suggest that this stage involves eliciting the patient's perception, especially in relation to the impact that their condition will have on their life. This can be gained through the use of the 90 second monologue described above. McGuigan (2009) suggests that in this stage the healthcare professional should establish what the patient already knows about their condition and what they want to know.

Marvel *et al.* (2011) note that there might be a fear of eliciting multiple concerns at one time. However, Detering *et al.* (2010) identify that in clarifying the patient's understanding of their illness and treatment options, understanding values and beliefs and goals of care, and clarifying their wishes the conversation can be positive and productive for the patient, family and care professionals.

Once the patient has had the opportunity to present their concerns there might be a need for information-giving, which should include adequate information that is honest and clear (Roman, 2007). It should avoid the use of jargon (McGuire, 2009) and there should be a move away from the delivery of messages and a move towards asking questions and exploring how the person is making sense of their world (Krumberger, 2003). The use of metaphors and analogies in these conversations may enhance communication, but they must be used honestly and accurately (Casarett *et al.*, 2009).

At this stage family and carer values can also be explored. The families or carers, their experiences in relation to decision making and how they came to that decision should be explored, so that the healthcare professionals can identify any lack in the information or misunderstanding in relation to the disease and/or treatment and support those decisions (Casarett *et al.*, 2009).

The conversation should be person-centred and address the needs and concerns of the person at that point of their journey with their condition (Barnes and Armstrong, 2010). Each patient, even with the same condition, will be different and each conversation will be different for different patients.

Dealing with emotions

Emotions might be strong in these conversations (Gallagher 2010) as we discuss sensitive issues. Sometimes nurses and other healthcare professionals struggle with the patient who shows their emotion through crying or anger and there can be a tendency to avoid such emotions so as not to damage the patient (Bratass *et al.*, 2008).

Barnes and Armstrong (2010) acknowledge that patients showing emotion through crying are difficult, challenging, demanding and stressful for the healthcare professional and can be 'hard work'. There might be a fear on the part of the healthcare professional of eliciting patients' emotions due to personal experiences and emotional responses to clinical situations, leading them to avoid such situations (Sheldon *et al.*, 2006). However, in this situation it is important to acknowledge the emotion (McGuigan, 2009). Part of the role in these difficult conversations includes giving emotional support to our patients (Duhamel and Dupuis, 2004).

When emotions are in the form of anger (which Lown (2007) identifies as a 'syndrome' of thoughts, feelings and physiological reactions) the relationship can be challenged. Professionals need to mange their own feelings, maintain appropriate boundaries and sustain their capacity for empathy. Lown goes on to suggest that often this anger is due to the patient's sense of vulnerability, diminished sense of self or disempowerment in the situation. McGuigan (2009) suggests that here the professional carer uses verbal or non-verbal warning signs in order to deal with these emotions.

When the patient is crying or showing visible signs of distress there can be a tendency, as Gordon *et al.* (2009) note, to control the conversation by controlling the topic and flow of the conversation in order to protect our patients and selves. As McGuigan (2009) identified, some nurses find that they avoid asking difficult questions as they might be emotionally distressing to the professional. In these situations Krumberger (2003) states that we need to review our own feelings. When there is a need to communicate bad news they suggest that this is given sensitively and that any distress is acknowledged.

Empathy

Duhamel and Dupuis (2004) state that empathy is 'acknowledging the experience of the illness'. Frankel and Stein (1999, p. 84) state that 'In the context of the clinician–patient relationship, empathy requires identifying a patient's emotional state accurately, naming it, and responding to it appropriately'.

Herbert *et al.* (2001) stressed the importance of empathy in these conversations. This can be through providing the information empathetically and openly whilst supporting the patient's choice (Casarett *et al.*, 2009).

Gordon *et al.* (2009) identified that nurses often talk in a functional manner so that they control the conversation. They do this by controlling the topic and flow of the conversation. This, they suggest, might be through the use of closed questions or in relation to the pressure of time in the institutional context. Frankel and Stein

(1999) highlight the importance of demonstrating appropriate empathy and being aware of your own reactions during conversations.

Joint decision making

Frankel and Stein (1999), McGuigan (2009) and Krumberger (2003) in their approaches to these conversations also identify the need for joint decision making. Gallagher *et al.* (2010) identified the importance of framing the conversation to reach an agreement, where the power structure belongs to everyone and not just the healthcare provider. If advance decisions, statements or care plans are developed they should be realistic and include the care that the patient has decided upon. These should be made by the patient once they have been fully informed as to the options and realistic wishes that can be carried out should the patient lose capacity at any stage of their illness to make that decision at the time.

Questioning

Gordon *et al.* (2009) and Georgaca and Avdi (2009) note that nurses may control the conversation when they are faced with difficult issues, as noted above. They suggest that this can be done by using closed questions and creating asymmetry in their interactions with the patient, controlling the topic and flow of the conversation. Again this might be an attempt to avoid those emotional situations and protect themselves against their own vulnerability. However, in this situation the patient must be the focus and as a result nurses and other healthcare professionals must be prepared to take the conversation as it comes and address the issues whilst maintaining the patient's agenda throughout the conversation. The use of open-ended questions is the most appropriate method to allow for this, and Marvel *et al.* (2011) suggested following each solicitation with a focused open-ended question. They provide the example of 'Tell us more about the leg pain'. Then they suggest reverting to another open-ended solicitation and giving the example 'Anything else?'. This can then be followed with closed questions to obtain further specific information.

Avoiding pitfalls

Mauksch *et al.* (2008) note many pitfalls in the conversations that need to be guarded against, such as too much small talk, dominance of the agenda by the healthcare professional, cognitive shortcuts, premature closure and own preoccupations. McGuigan (2009) also advises the healthcare professional to prevent misunderstanding and unrealistic expectations. These negative aspects of the conversations can be guarded against by building trust and good rapport with the patient, using mindful practice, maintaining focus on the conversations, looking for cues and using micro skills such as summarising and reflecting on the discussion to make sure the agenda is still the patient's and that both the patient and healthcare professional are agreeing with and understanding what is being said.

Identifying support networks

Duhamel and Dupuis (2004) acknowledge the existence and expertise of the family and unpaid carers. However, we recognise that this might cause additional problems when other members of the family have different points of view. Krumberger (2003) states that we should explore the family's and carers' values and experiences and recognise that each point of view is valid, and suggests that their feelings are also acknowledged. Casarret *et al.* (2009) highlight the importance of supporting family and their choices under what are difficult and emotionally trying circumstances for all of them involved with the care provision.

McGuigan (2009), in her ten-stage strategy for difficult conversations, notes the importance of identifying the patient's network and the importance of letting them know what support is available.

Closing the conversation and what will happen next

Frankel and Stein (1999) also identify the importance of investing in the end of these conversations. They note the importance of providing education and delivering diagnosis information in the final stage of the conversation. McGuigan's (2009) ten-stage strategy finishes with identifying, for the patient, what will happen next.

Reflecting on the conversations

England (2005) noted that nurses reflect more on the ways in which they communicate and empower clients in the direction of health. They go on to note that a well-honed conversation is an expression of critical thinking, communication and intervention skills that are indispensable to the delivery of patient-focused care. McGuigan (2009) highlights the importance of reflecting on these difficult and challenging conversations and also notes that it is self-awareness that enables the nurse to observe how to react to particular situations and the effect that they have on an individual on the situation and on others. Reflection should not only take into consideration the actual conversation but also explore the health professional's reactions and dealing with the patients, families/carers and their own emotions. Clinical supervision or practice support is a useful and constructive approach to reflecting with others (Lillyman and Ghaye, 2007). Through this process collective wisdom can be obtained that will assist the healthcare professional to develop these advanced communication skills (Ghaye *et al.*, 2008).

One conversation will never be the same as another in this situation. However, through the process of reflecting on these conversations we can develop the communication skills, become more prepared, confident, deal with time constraints, pick up those important patient cues, set and follow the patient's agenda and empower patients to take control over their care journey. In Chapter 6 we will see an example of such a conversation.

References

Barnes, S. and Armstrong, E. (2010) Conversations after right hemisphere brain damage: motivations for applying conversation analysis. *Clinical Linguistics and Phonetics*, **24**(1), 55–69.

Bratass, H., Thorsnes, S. and Hargie, O. (2009) Cancer nurses narrating after conversations with cancer outpatients how do nurses' roles and patients' perspectives appear in the nurses' narratives? *Scandinavian Journal of Caring Science*, **23**, 767–74.

British Medical Association (2007) *Advance Decisions and Proxy Decision Making in Medical Treatment and Research*. BMA, London.

British Medical Association (2009) *End of Life Decisions*. BMA, London.

Casarett, D., Pickard, A., Fishman, J. M., Alexander, S. C., Arnold, R. M., Pollak, K. I. and Tulsky, J. A. (2009) Can metaphors and analogies improve communication with seriously ill patients? *Journal of Palliative Medicine*, **13**(3), 255–60.

Detering, K. M., Hancock, A. D., Reade, M. C. and Silvester, W. (2010) The impact of advance care planning on end of life care in elderly patients. Randomised control trial. *British Medical Journal*, doi 10.1136/bmj.c1345.

Drew, P., Chatwin, J. and Collins, S. (2001) Conversations analysis: a method for research into interactions between patients and health care professionals. *Health Expectations*, **4**, 58–70.

Duhamel, F. and Dupuis, F. (2004) Guaranteed returns: investing in a conversation with families of patients with cancer. *Clinical Journal of Oncology Nursing*, **8**(1), 68–71.

England, M. (2005) Analysis of nurse conversation: methodology of the process recording. *Journal of Psychiatric and Mental Health Nursing*, **12**, 661–71.

Frankel, E. M. and Stein, T. (1999) Getting the most out of the clinical encounter: the four habits model. *The Permanente Journal*, **3**(3), 70–88.

Gallagher, S. M., Steadman, A. K. and Gallagher, S. M. (2010) Tackling tough topics: recognising societal bias as a barrier to crucial conversations. *Bariatric Times*, **7**(6), 24–8.

Georgaca, E. and Avdi, E. (2009) Evaluating and talking cure: the contribution of narrative, discourse and conversation analysis to psychotherapy assessment. *Qualitative Research in Psychology*, **6**, 233–47.

Ghaye, T., Melander-Wikman, A., Kaisare, M., Chambers, P., Bergmark, U., Kostenius, C. and Lillyman, S. (2008) Participatory and appreciative action and reflection (PAAR) – democratizing reflective practices. *Reflective Practice*, **9**(4), 361–98.

Gordon, C., Ellis-Hill, C. and Ashburn, A. (2009) The use of conversational analysis: nurse patient interaction in communication disability after stroke. *Journal of Advanced Nursing*, **65**(3), 544–53.

Haigh, N. (2005) Everyday conversations as a context for professional learning and development. *International Journal for Academic Development*, **10**(1), 3–16.

Herbert, R. S., Jenckes, M. W., Ford, D. E., O'Connor, D. R. and Copper, L. A. (2001) Patient perspective on spirituality and the patient physician relationship. *Journal of General Internal Medicine*, **16**, 685–92.

Koropchack, C. M., Pollack, K. I., Arnold, R. M., Alexander, S. C., Skinner, C. S., Olsen, M. K., Jeffreys, A. S., Rodriguez, K. L., Abernethy, A. P. and Tulsky, J. A. (2006) Studying communication in oncologist-patient encounters. The SCOPE trial. *Palliative Medicine*, **20**, 813–19.

Krumberger, J. (2003) Difficult conversations. *RN*, **66**(11), 2–3.

Langewitz, W., Denz, M., Keller, A., Kiss, A., Ruttimann, S. and Wossmer, B. (2002) Spontaneous talking time at the start of consultations in outpatient clinic: cohort study. *British Medical Journal*, **325**, 682–3.

Lillyman, S. and Ghaye, T. (2007) *Effective Clinical Supervision: The Role of Reflection*, 2nd edn. Quay Books, London.

Lown, B. A. (2007) Difficult conversations; anger in the clinician–patient/family relationships. *Southern Medical Journal*, **100**(1), 33–9.

Marvel, K., Epstein, R. M., Flowers, K. and Beckman, H. B. (2011) Soliciting the patient's agenda. Have we improved? *Journal of the American Medical Association*, **281**(3), 283–7.

Mauksch, L. B., Dugdale, D. C., Dodson, S. and Epstein, R. (2008) Relationship, communication and efficiency in the medical encounter. *Archives of Internal Medicine*, **168**(13), 1387–95.

McDonald, G., Vickers, M. H., Mohan, S., Wilkes, L. and Jackson, D. (2010) Workplace conversations: building and maintaining collaborative capital. *Contemporary Nurse*, **36**(1–2), 96–105.

McGuigan, D. (2009) Communicating bad news to patient: a reflective approach. *Nursing Standard*, **23**(31), 51–6.

Murray, S. A., Sheikh, A. and Thomas, K. (2006) Advance care planning in primary care: uncomfortable but likely to engender hope rather than dispel it. *British Medical Journal*, **333**, 868–9.

Rabinowitz, I., Luzzatti, R., Tamir, A. and Reis, S. (2004) Length of patient's monologue, rate of completion and relation to other components of the clinical encounter: observational intervention study in primary care. *British Medical Journal*, **328**, 501–2.

Roman, L. M. (2007) Finding the words: how to handle difficult conversations. *RN*, **70**(3), 34–8.

Sheldon, L. K., Barrett, R. and Ellington, L. (2006) Difficult conversations in nursing. *Journal of Nursing Scholarship*, **38**(2), 141–7.

Singer, P. A., Robertson, G. and Roy D. J. (1996) Bioethics for clinicians 6: advance care planning. *Canadian Medical Association Journal*, **155**, 168–92.

Tapp, D. M. (2001) Conserving the validity of suffering: addressing family constraints to illness conversation. *Nursing Inquiry*, **8**(4), 254–63.

Tulsky, J. A. (2005) Beyond advance directives. *Journal of the American Medical Association*, **294**(3), 359–65.

Uitterhoeve, R., Bensing, J., Diven, E., Donders, R., deMulder, P. and Achterberg, T. (2009) Nurse–patient communication in cancer care: does responding to patient's cues predict patient satisfaction with communication? *Psycho-Oncology*, **18**, 1060–8.

Weiner, J. S. and Efferen, L. S. (2005) Recognition and communication. *Chest*, **127**(6), 1886–8.

Wright, L. M. and Leahey, M. (2000) *Nurses and Families: a Guide to Family Assessment and Intervention*, 3rd edn. FA Davies, Philadelphia.

CHAPTER 6

A caring moment with Peter

Ruth Hardie

Caring moments are not just experiences we live through, but ones we need to analyse and use to identify the aesthetic knowledge and experiential learning acquired. It is through these reflective practices that we give ourselves opportunities to further improve clinical practice, draw upon and use scientific knowledge appropriately, and ultimately develop and provide evidence of an 'expert' practice in action (Ghaye and Lillyman, 2006).

The caring moment

One morning, when taking the opportunity to prepare for a busy afternoon clinic by looking through the medical records of those patients booked in for pre-operative assessment, one of the staff nurses on the ward ran into my office asking if I would go to the ward as one of the patients was calling for me. The staff nurse appeared worried, so I instantly stopped my work and hastened to the ward.

There seemed a lot of commotion on the ward: the noise level was high and my attention was drawn to the gentleman in the corner bed, who was shouting my name loudly. Knowing him well, I went instantly to his side. Peter was very agitated and distressed, clinging to my hand he exclaimed, 'I'm dying aren't I? Ruth you have always been straight with me, tell me the truth now, I'm dying aren't I?' Sitting next to Peter, and taking both of his hands into mine while looking straight into his eyes, I spoke softly to try to calm and reassure him, saying, 'I can feel your distress, and want to help you, but before we can address your fears let us try to make you feel a little calmer so that you can concentrate on what we discuss'. I continued to speak softly, asking Peter to breathe slowly and deeply and reminding him of our open and honest relationship. I reassured him that his questions would be answered with the same honesty.

When Peter was calmer, the curtains around his bed were closed to ensure a little more privacy. Returning to my seated position facing Peter, and holding his hands in mine whilst maintaining eye contact, I asked him what had caused his distress. He responded by saying that he had an overwhelming feeling that he was going to die imminently and that he wanted someone to tell him honestly if this was going to happen. My response was, 'Peter, what do you know about your illness?'. He said, 'I know I've got cancer and that it has spread into other parts of my body'. I confirmed that this was true, and that this meant he was very ill. He then said, 'It is going to kill me isn't it?'. My reply was, 'Yes Peter, the cancer will probably cause you to die, but before that, you have got a lot of living to do'. He responded, 'What do you mean?'. 'You are seriously ill with advanced metastatic cancer, and you are very weak, but you have a wonderful family and you have told me that you want to spend more time with them. Having a lot of living to do means that you should spend this stage in your life living, and doing those things which are most important for you. Talk to your family; say the things you want to say and do the things you want to do. Make every moment special, live life with the cancer, rather than die with the cancer.'

At this, Peter silently cried, then squeezed my hands. He then asked me to call his wife: he wanted to see her and tell her that he loved her. Peter insisted on my staying with him while his wife came to the ward. He held my hand firmly and whispered, 'Please don't leave'. As I spoke softly and calmly to Peter, talking about all of the wonderful things he had told me about his wife and children, concentrating on the laughter, love and fun they shared together, he began to smile. When his wife arrived on the ward Peter was calmer and they held on to each other, both silently crying.

When I attempted to leave, Peter asked if I could stay for a while. He said 'I still need some of your strength'. He then turned to his wife and said, 'I feel more in control now. I know I'm going to die, but it will be when I am ready. I need to spend some more time with you and the boys first; Ruth has helped me see that. I love you, and want to tell you, I want you to remember that when I am gone'. They held each other again and, although there were tears, there was also a great sense of happiness. Peter soon relaxed back into his pillows exhausted with emotion. He squeezed my hand and said, 'You can go now, I thank you for your help, you have given me back my life'.

On leaving the room, my own feelings and tears surfaced, a feeling that I had done so little, but glad that it was helpful, if only in a small way.

Peter died very peacefully in his wife's arms two weeks later, after saying his goodbyes to all his family and friends. At Peter's funeral his wife hugged me and thanked me for helping them, saying that I was in the right profession.

My reflections on this moment

My role on the unit was that of a nurse practitioner. My job entailed seeing all elective patients prior to surgery to undertake a holistic assessment, to assess their nursing, medical, psychological, social and spiritual needs. This form of assessment helps establish trust in the nurse–patient relationship, intervening by listening and collecting information that will be useful in the planning of patient care (Allport *et al.*, 1985). This in-depth assessment allowed me to get to know the patient and their families well, and ensured preparation of the interdisciplinary team for the patient's admission. Assessment also prepared the patient for surgery or tests by educating them about what was involved in the procedures and what was to be expected post-operatively (Hardie, 1993). Patients benefited from this consultation as they were more willing to discuss problems with a nurse than a doctor, as the problem of 'not wanting to waste the doctor's time' still persists (McLaughlin, 1978).

Peter had been one of these patients. When he first came to the assessment clinic he had little understanding of his forthcoming operation, but had openly told me that he hadn't liked to ask the doctor, as he felt that he was busy in clinic. That was over a year ago, and Peter and his wife had been back to my clinic many times, where we had honestly discussed his invasive cancer. He had found that some members of the interdisciplinary team had difficulty discussing his disease and used avoidance techniques to prevent entering conversation. We had discussed that this was a form of defence mechanism to protect themselves against the pain they felt (Lichter, 1987). Peter had always commented that he wanted to be fully informed of his disease as his way of keeping control. The consultant involved with Peter's care acknowledged my communication skills and my specialist knowledge. He felt that the needs of the patients concerning communicating bad news and prognosis were met more effectively by a consultation with me rather than a doctor. This is true interdisciplinary teamwork, where there is willingness to share and, indeed, give up exclusive claims to specialised knowledge and authority (Barr, 1997). The consultant acknowledged that another professional could meet the needs of the patient more effectively. Over that year, Peter and I had developed a therapeutic relationship based on trust, agreeing with Kaye (1996) that trust depends on reputation, competence and liking, which depend mainly on listening.

Reflection-on-practice

Reflecting on my actions helps me to make sense of what I did, did not do, might have done and what I might do when encountering moments like this again. On reflection, my purpose was to ensure that Peter had been helped to maintain his quality of life. Kubler-Ross (1970) believes that all patients know the seriousness of their illness, and that what many patients and their families want is permission to be open about their worries and anxieties.

Relaxation techniques were used to calm Peter sufficiently to enable us to have a conversation without causing more distress. Experience has taught me that when a person is distressed they take in very little of a conversation. Choosing my words, as our open and honest relationship seemed important to Peter, I faced him so that he could see my facial expression showing my concern. I held his hands, as a caring touch demonstrates empathy and is one way of 'giving permission' to patients and relatives to reveal their anxieties and distress (Autton, 1989). It was obvious from Peter's answer to my question – 'What do you know about your illness?' – that he had a firm understanding of the nature of his disease. He was feeling a sense of panic about his impending death. I personally agree with Yalom (1980), that although dying is considered a time of crisis, it can also be an opportunity for change and positive growth. It was important to me that Peter did not lose all hope, and that however bad my news, which confirmed his fear, it was most important to offer some positive, truthful message. Hope needs an object; setting realistic goals with a patient is one way of restoring and maintaining hope (Twycross, 1997). When trying to maintain realistic goals with Peter, it seemed appropriate to concentrate on the positive aspects of his life which were achievable. With patients close to death, hope tends to focus on being, rather than achieving, and on relationships with others (Twycross, 1997); in Peter's case I focused on the relationship with his family.

An important intention when working with Peter was to enable him to maintain control over his life. Working to achieve this meant acquiring an in-depth knowledge and understanding of the physical, emotional and psychological developments in the process of dying (Russell and Sander, 1998). From my experience, and from discussions with the medical team about Peter's condition, it seemed that Peter did not have long to live. What was important was that with my skills of empathy, anticipation and communication he was helped to adapt to his new circumstances (Pullen, 1995). Peter acknowledged that I had made the appropriate intervention by thanking me for giving him back his life, and ultimately he maintained control right until the end of his life, dying peacefully in his wife's arms.

Reflecting on my own professional development, the three main characteristics which have developed throughout my nursing career, and which were used to help Peter, are congruence, unconditional positive regard, and sensitive empathetic understanding. Corey (1991) believes that congruence implies that the nurse is real: genuine, integrated and authentic, without a false front; and that the inner experience and outer expression of that experience match and that the nurse can openly express feelings and attitudes that are present in the relationship with the patient. Congruence was demonstrated by my own belief that death is part of life's journey and everyone should be enabled to live life fully throughout this journey. Peter will have identified that my inner beliefs matched my spoken word.

Unconditional positive regard is where the nurse communicates a deep and genuine caring for the patient as a person. The caring is unconditional, valuing and accepting the patient without placing stipulations on the acceptance (Corey, 1991). When Peter called for me, he had the confidence in our relationship to know that he would be accepted as he was; troubled, distressed, frightened and needing support, and that I would not judge him, but just try to help him.

Empathetic understanding was offered by taking account of Peter's experience and feelings sensitively and accurately as they were revealed in the moment-to-moment interaction, and demonstrating my understanding of these feelings (Corey, 1991). Peter's fear of facing death was palpable, as well as his sense of loss at losing his family and his sense of losing control as the cancer weakened his body. Having empathy with these feelings enabled me to help Peter address all of these issues.

My acceptance of Peter and his condition was communicated by the quality of my presence with him, my calm approach, my willingness to answer any of his questions, my body language and my touch. All of these attributes gave him confidence and energy, which enabled him to take control over his life. The presence of one who can talk calmly and unemotionally about death, who listens quietly and conveys understanding, goes beyond words, and speaks more loudly about life and love than any words spoken, no matter how affectionately or eloquently (Autton, 1989). The incident appeared to take a short time; in reality, it lasted approximately one and a half hours. When I eventually left the room, I felt a number of emotions, but, significantly, I felt a strange sense of peace – a sense that all that could be given was given and that somehow Peter's needs were met. Nursing is concerned with meeting the needs of the person and the family. For nursing to be effective, these needs have to be patient-centred, which places a responsibility on the nurse to treat each patient as a unique individual (Holt, 1995).

Walton (1995) believes that working as a nurse inherently provokes anxiety, as you are continually confronting issues concerning the meaning of life and the 'spirit' of people in acute distress and adversity. He feels that the nurse's challenge is to accept and work with a more aware view of oneself, and your own issues, and be able to continue to undertake the nursing, caring responsibility of working with patients as people rather than cases of clinical conditions. To cope with such underlying pressures, and to look after yourself at the same time, takes strength, personal insight and energy.

Walton (1995) believes that to do this you need to know who you are, what you stand for, and the values and beliefs that you hold dear. He goes on to say that our core beliefs are our source of inner regard, strength and cohesion, and these will drive us to tackle many situations, guiding us in taking action and responding to events. Identifying my core beliefs through reflection and exploration has helped influence and change my practice. I have learnt to value myself as a significant person, with values and feelings that are important factors in giving care (Johns, 1995). Acknowledging my core beliefs when reflecting on this time with Peter has helped identify what influenced my decision-making.

How reflecting on this caring moment has helped me understand my essential caring values

Value 1: Respect
I try to value everyone I encounter, respecting them as an individual and treating them as I wish to be treated. Peter's wishes were for honest communication and respect as the intelligent professional he was, and to be given full information of the nature of his disease at every stage. This openness influenced Peter's reason for asking for me, knowing that I would respond to his wishes.

Value 2: Peace
I value finding peace in my life and helping others to find peace in theirs. It was important to me to help Peter find peace in his life, to become more accepting of his condition so that he could live life with cancer, rather than die with cancer. This helped him to find some hope and to identify some realistic goals, enabling him to take more control over his life, which ultimately, I believe, enabled him to find peace.

Value 3: Quality
I value being able to deliver quality nursing care and empowering others to do the same. My role of nurse practitioner helped improve the quality of nursing care for the whole team, as it enabled greater communication between the patient and the team. By undertaking a holistic assessment, including the nursing, medical, psychological, social and spiritual aspects of care, I could act as the patient's

advocate, helping them to address their individual needs. Holt (1995) believes that assessment is possibly the most vital stage of the nursing process, as it acts as a basis for all other stages, and is essential for nurses to be able to plan good quality, individualised care.

Value 4: Time

I value being able to provide time for others, to address individual need and time for myself. With the pressures of working and current staff shortages within a busy acute Trust hospital, many nurses feel that they do not have enough time to deliver quality care. The role of nurse practitioner enables independent working and not being tied into the same constraints as the nursing team. Being responsible for my own working patterns gave me the flexibility to give Peter the time he needed. However, I acknowledge that this would not always be the case. For example, if Peter had called for me in the afternoon, I would have been in the middle of a busy clinic and would not have been able to go to the ward. Having time to address patients' psychological and spiritual needs is an essential part of my work. Reflecting on this incident has caused me to identify within myself a shift of priorities, in both my private life and professional practice, and has influenced my decision-making.

Value 5: Nursing

I value nursing as a profession and the contribution it makes to society. Nurse practitioners are viewed by some as a cheap alternative to fill the gaps left by doctor shortages (Emmerson, 1996). When setting up the role of nurse practitioner there remained a strong belief in nursing: the reasoning behind advancing my nursing practice was to improve the quality of healthcare for patients. To this end, the medical model was incorporated into my nursing practice to ensure holism, rather than adopting the medical model to the detriment of nursing (Castledine, 1996a). It is my belief that the work of nurses is to: care for patients by maintaining client dignity and self-respect; tailor care to meet individual need; educate to provide appropriate information and support; ensure competent, safe, evidence-based practice; continually evaluate practice and work collaboratively with the interdisciplinary team; and act as the patient advocate (Scott, 1997). Through the advanced role, education, demonstration of my skills and collaboration with the interdisciplinary team, I was given the opportunity and empowerment to meet most of the patients' needs. In Peter's situation, there were the knowledge base, skills and authority to discuss the nature of his disease and its progress.

Value 6: Care

I value being able to care for patients' relatives, family, friends and myself. Caring is not exclusive to nursing, but perhaps is the only profession that has caring as its central focus (Wright, 1995). Through this meeting with Peter and his wife, there was the opportunity to demonstrate my feelings for them through empathy, congruence and unconditional positive regard. Johns (1995) believes that as nurses have become more experienced, they have tended to give away the more caring aspects of their work to junior and unqualified staff. With the advanced nursing role, caring has remained a central focus: hopefully, acting as a role model for more junior nurses will ensure that caring remains one of their core beliefs. Reflection on this caring moment and discussion of the same during clinical supervision has helped me care for myself, by developing individual insight and self-awareness. This I feel has enabled me to lead a more fulfilling lifestyle (Copp, 1988).

Value 7: Limitations

I value being able to acknowledge my own limitations. On reflection, I would not have changed the essential nature of my actions throughout this moment with Peter. However, one aspect which was not addressed was the needs of my nursing colleagues. It could be argued that as Peter asked for me instead of his named nurse, her role was eroded and her responsibility devalued. In this instance, Peter's named nurse was a junior staff nurse who did not have the knowledge and skills to meet Peter's needs. What should have followed this incident was a team discussion to enable all the team members to develop their expertise in this aspect of patient care. The role of the advanced nurse practitioner should include acting as a consultant and educator in all matters relating to his or her particular chosen field and role (Castledine, 1996b). When reflecting as to why this did not happen on this occasion there were a few issues to consider:

- The incident was personally exhausting; therefore I needed time and space to recover to enable me to prepare for continued work.
- It was an extremely busy shift for the nurses and they could not release themselves from their workload to undergo a teaching session.
- Time was needed to reflect on the incident for personal learning.
- When broaching the subject of discussing death with a patient, many colleagues shy away as they find it distressing to be confronted with questions they cannot or are not permitted to answer (Lichter, 1987). Therefore the timing of such discussion is crucial in order to provide appropriate support for team members.

Thinking again

My learning from this experience enabled me to identify improvements in my practice. I have not tied myself up in knots trying to use someone else's model of reflection. Rather, I have been conscious of two things: first, the importance of knowing my professional values (Ghaye *et al.*, 1996), and second, by trying to build a coherent and professional story there is a growing awareness within me of the importance of the present moment, and living life with an acceptance of its foreseeable end. The awareness that death is a normal part of life helps to remove the fear surrounding it. At the same time, it enhances the importance of valuing each moment, living life to the full knowing that it will end. This awareness develops the importance of giving time to meeting patients' deepest needs, enabling them to live their life to the full within the limitation of their disease.

This reflection has changed the direction of my career in nursing, as there developed in me a greater desire to help patients fulfil their hopes and, through education, to share this knowledge with my professional colleagues. It could be argued that areas within an acute Trust hospital need people with the ability to communicate effectively with the dying patient and relative. However, my recent move to a hospice environment is helping my ambition to fulfil the following. It is an attempt to try to summarise some of the essential attributes of patient care. It is a statement of intent and of value. It is therefore something I keep with me and try to live out in my work. I feel that:

> Patients should be enabled to live until they die, at their own maximum potential, performing to the limit of their physical activity and mental capacity, with control and independence wherever possible. They should be recognised as the unique individuals they are and helped to live as part of their family (however this might be defined) and in other relationships with some awareness from those around of their own hopes and expectations and of what has deepest meaning for them.

References

Allport *et al.* (1985) as cited in Holt, P. (1995) Role of questioning skills in patient assessment. *British Journal of Nursing*, **4**(19), 1145.

Autton, N. (1989) *Touch and Exploration*. Darton, Longman and Todd, London.

Barr, O. (1997) Interdisciplinary teamwork: consideration of the challenges. *British Journal of Nursing*, **5**(17), 1005–10.

Castledine, G. (1996a) Are British nurses lethargic? *British Journal of Nursing*, **5**(1), 51–3.

Castledine, G. (1996b) The role and criteria of an advanced nurse practitioner. *British Journal of Nursing*, **5**(5), 289.

Copp, G. (1988) as cited in Butterworth, T. and Faugier, J. (eds.) (1992) *Clinical Supervision and Mentorship in Nursing*. Chapman & Hall, London.

Corey, G. (1991) *Theory and Practice of Counseling and Psychotherapy*, 4th edn. Brooks/Cole Publishing Company, Pacific Grove, CA.

Emmerson, P. (1996) Are nurse practitioners merely substitute doctors? *Professional Nurse*, **11**(5), 326.

Ghaye, T. and Lillyman, S. (2006) *Learning Journals and Critical Incidents: Reflective Practice for Healthcare Professionals*, 2nd edn. Quay Books, London.

Ghaye, T., Cuthbert, S. and Danai, K. (1996) *Professional Values: Being a Professional. Self-Supported Learning Experiences for Healthcare Professionals*. Pentaxion Press Ltd, Newcastle upon Tyne.

Hardie, R. (1993) Day surgery assessment nurse. *Journal of One-Day Surgery*, **2**(3), 19–20.

Holt, P. (1995) Role of questioning skills in patient assessment. *British Journal of Nursing*, **4**(19), 145.

Johns, C. (1995) The value of reflective practice for nursing. In: *Reflection and Action for Health Care Professionals: A Reader* (ed. T. Ghaye) (1996) Pentaxion Press Ltd, Newcastle upon Tyne.

Kaye, P. (1996) *Breaking Bad News (pocket book): A Ten-Step Approach*. EPL Publications, London.

Kubler-Ross, E. (1970) *On Death and Dying*. Tavistock, London.

Lichter, I. (1987) *Communication in Cancer Care*. Churchill Livingstone, Edinburgh.

McLaughlin, F. (1978) as cited in Marsden, J. (1995) Setting up nurse practitioner roles: issues in practice. *British Journal of Nursing*, **4**(16), 952.

Pullen, F. (1995) Advocacy: a specialist practitioner role. *British Journal of Nursing*, **4**(5), 275–8.

Russell, P. and Sander, R. (1998) Palliative care: promoting the concept of a healthy death. *British Journal Nursing*, **7**(5), 256–61.

Scott, H. (1997) The importance of core values in nursing. *British Journal of Nursing*, **6**(11), 604.

Twycross, R. (1997) *Introducing Palliative Care*, 2nd edn. Radcliffe Medical Press, Oxford and New York.

Walton, M. (1995) *Managing Yourself On and Off the Ward*. Blackwell Science Ltd, Oxford.

Wright, S. (1995) The role of the nurse: extended or expanded? *Nursing Standard*, **10/9**(33), 27.

Yalom, I. (1980) *Existential Psychotherapy*. Basic Books, New York.

CHAPTER 7

A caring moment with Rachel

Val Chapman

In this chapter I intend to illuminate the notion of a caring moment by drawing on an example from the broad field of educare (a wide range of caring professions, including social work and school teaching). In doing so, I am trying to make the point that there is much to learn from doing this. This is a particular example, grounded in educational practice, with a focus on lived experience, reflection and learning. Although particular in kind, I am going to suggest that there are a number of important and interesting principles, of a general nature, that we can glean from this that are relevant to healthcare professionals. It is a reversal in the way we might think about a caring moment. It does not look at caring moments from within healthcare but from an allied and related perspective. In this sense, it is an 'outside-looking-in' view. It is also an illustration of the principle of inter-professional learning.

The story of Rachel's cat

An observer's perspective: me looking from the 'outside in'

Rachel came into the Centre, responded quietly (eyes floored) to my 'Good morning, Rachel' and sat bolt upright at the table in front of me, her eyes fixed on her hands which were clenched tightly in her lap. In that short trip across the room her body language had shrieked of tightly controlled anguish, the absolute economy of movement signalling a taut restraint of inner turmoil.

The three boys entered next, boisterous, bantering, chorusing, 'Good morning, Mrs Taylor' in that obligatory school, sing-song style. Chair legs were knocked against tables, papers were rustled and pencils dropped as they busied themselves getting out the paraphernalia of learning.

'Morning boys.' She rose from her seat and moved a nearby chair to sit next to the small, sad child who sat stiffly, her back rigid with tension.

'What's wrong, Rachel?' she inquired gently.

A ragged intake of breath prefaced the wobbly-voiced response, 'Nnn...

nothing, Miss'.

'Rachel, look at me sweetheart.... What's the matter?' she asked, searching her face for clues.

Maybe it was the endearment, or maybe it was the teacher's arm around her shoulders that cracked Rachel's resolve. Big, fat tears welled up and wetted her lashes before slipping down her cheeks leaving shiny damp trails, evidence other misery, in their wake.

Gulping and sobbing, she finally managed to hiccup out the words, 'Oh... ohh... Miss, Benjie's d... uhh... hh... ead'. Just as she completed her statement, her older sister, Rebecca, entered the room and, hearing her sister's last words, she too dissolved into noisy tears.

The three lads looked on, concern vying with morbid speculation as to the cause of the cat's demise, while Mrs Taylor made space on her lap for two small bodies in need of a motherly cuddle.

Bit by bit, the story emerged of how poor Benjie had been found stiff on the lawn that morning. Rachel explained how they hadn't really worried when he hadn't come home the previous night, since he occasionally stayed with Auntie B, an elderly neighbour who lived alone and sometimes used to borrow Benjie for company, and who 'spoiled him rotten with love'.

Gradually, the girls began to calm down as they told the group all about Benjie and his life with their family. They talked about the toys he liked to play with, sunny places he favoured for sleeping, and his bits of endearing naughtiness – the kind of snippets of life history that settle deep into a family's personal folklore and are recounted time and time again, the act of repeated sharing which exudes the glue that refreshes and strengthens a family's bonds as the years continue to pass by.

A little while later, just as the girls had reclaimed control over their voices and Mrs Taylor thought the emotional storm clouds were lifting, Rebecca suddenly wailed, '... and then... this morning... just before we left for school... Mummy put his bowl... **in the bin!**'. Huge, racking sobs ensued from both girls, their mother's pragmatic action having obviously conveyed the full impact of death's finality.

The group's planned learning activities for the morning were shelved. Instead, Mrs Taylor settled the group in the comfy corner, where Rachel and Rebecca were encouraged to talk further about and celebrate all the good bits of Benjie's life.

The boys (not normally known for their ability to sustain attention) listened avidly and were quick to join in with their own memories of having lost a pet, how much they, too, had cried; and one having 'even had a grandma who died once!'. Led by their teacher, they talked about memories and she explained about obituaries, about how language could capture the essence of a person or a creature. Quieter now, and in control of their grief, the two girls decided they'd like to commemorate Benjie's life by writing an obituary which they could take home to share with their parents and Auntie B.

For the moment, with the distant sound of children's voices echoing from their PE lesson in the playground, peace and equilibrium were restored.

The sort of moment described above is certainly not unusual. From my perspective, the practitioner's genuine concern for her pupil (highlighted when she approached the child with a loving touch and gentle voice) was the defining 'caring moment'. The combined conscious and conscientious actions of sitting next to the child, touching and talking to her may have been instinctive, but the chosen course of action was one that was based on years of experience with and understanding of children. This caring moment captured in that snapshot of time revealed the quality of the individual at both a personal and professional level, and illustrates the nature of someone who is an extended professional.

While most parents can easily relate to the instinct to cuddle a hurting child, the drive to comfort another human being in need of help reveals a more generalisable quality that may be attributed to a broader population. For some, a caring manner may originate in deeply held religious or spiritual beliefs, while for others the concern may be the overt expression of morals which have been embedded in their psyche by their experiences during their upbringing.

Such concern for the welfare of others may be a natural empathy which some possess as a result of a high 'inter-personal' intelligence.[1] Gardner advocates the view that those who are most successful in life are not necessarily those who have strengths in the logical-mathematical and linguistic areas (these being the most commonly tested intelligences in schools), but those who have high inter- and intra-personal intelligence which afford sophisticated self-knowledge and an ability to understand and relate to others.

He illustrated his concept of inter-personal intelligence by the inclusion of a description of how Anne Sullivan managed the learning of Helen Keller, who was both blind and deaf. He believed that the key to Anne's miracle breakthrough into Helen's silent, unsighted world lay in her own insight into the 'person' of Helen Keller rather than any functional knowledge of methodology or therapeutic technique.

Since he claims that sound functioning of the brain's frontal lobes play a prominent role in inter-personal abilities and recognises that a secure parenting

---

1 Gardner (1993) argues that there are seven kinds of intelligence: musical, bodily-kinaes-thetic, spatial, intra-personal, logical-mathematical and linguistic.

experience and socialisation through interaction with others are also significant factors in the development of a high inter-personal intelligence, it is interesting to consider whether or not those with such backgrounds and brain biology are almost physiologically – if not sociologically – predestined to enter the caring professions.

But how did Mrs Taylor become the kind of person she is? What underpinned that caring moment? What experiences has she had in her own life which have brought her to this stage, where she is able to operate in such an ethically sensitive and humane way? Was it reflection on her own childhood experiences? Was it a conscious reflection on her personal ethical code of practice, its origin and its validity? Had she, as a young professional, looked at her practice and asked herself questions such as, Why do I behave like this? What am I trying to do? What do I believe in? Why are these values dear to me? What should I be doing in order to feel comfortable in my practice, to know that my workplace actions are supported by a clearly defined and firmly espoused set of values?

The carer's perspective

Well, I could see she was upset straight away-she didn't have to say anything, it was just obvious, wasn't it? She's always such a chirpy, sweet little thing, I knew it had to be something really significant.

Why did I act that way? Well... I know that we're supposed to get through the curriculum (and there's precious little time to manage that these days!), but, apart from being concerned about her (she's such a poppet) and just wanting to help her, there's absolutely no point trying to teach someone who's feeling like that, is there? They just won't take it in. No, I knew that I needed to sort it out straight away, she was obviously so upset. When you're a teacher you have to be concerned for the whole child, not just focus on the teaching aspect.

And as for the lads in the class, well, I have to keep a firm hand with them 'cause they're so easily distracted. I always have to make sure they are completely occupied with activities that they're challenged by and interested in otherwise their behaviour can be quite difficult. So I suppose all those things went through my mind really... the girls being upset, the boys' behaviour, the day's tasks....

... Yes, I suppose all of that flew through my mind and I chose what I saw as the best course of action for all of them – all of us, I mean. It worked out OK, I felt that we all learned something from the experience and I think it was really important to talk about their grief and dying. It can be so scary for children when they are confronted with death like that, don't you think? Everyone was fine after play and we got a lot done later that morning.

When a professional, either wittingly or unconsciously, is the architect of a caring moment, it is probable that such evident concern is the result of a cognizant adherence to a consciously espoused set of personal and professional values. Such care reflects a genuine professional commitment to living out one's values in one's workplace. It is interesting to note that despite Mrs Taylor's almost blasé acceptance of the incident as somewhat commonplace, her statement that 'we all learned something from the experience' indicates that she recognised that the event was imbued with a significance for possible revisions to her future practice. This kind of care is evidence of a reflective practitioner who is dedicated to constantly striving to improve her professional practice and who views each situation as one which can be learned from.

In any context, caring moments that occur may be described, either during or after the event, as critical incidents. Reflection on these has much to offer the practitioner. Although they may be snapshots of daily work, by examining them the effects of care on those involved can be seen, and interactions between colleagues can be highlighted. This also helps to make the important point that reflection-on-practice needs not to be reflection on the extra-ordinary but on the 'ordinary', the often taken-for-granted aspects of everyday practice. Reflection is not an exceptional activity brought out of the locker to try to 'solve' the problems and challenges posed by the extra-ordinary. There is much to learn from thinking again about and re-viewing the ordinary.

Though the tern 'critical incident' in healthcare or police arenas of work frequently describes a life-threatening situation, Tripp (1993) and Ghaye (1997) allow a wider interpretation of the terminology. Tripp (1993, p. 8) suggests that critical incidents are recognised or constructed:

> Incidents happen, but critical incidents are produced by the way we look at a situation, it is an interpretation of the significance of the event.

...and the incidents do not necessarily have to be life threatening or dramatic (Chapman, 1998, p. 33):

> It is not always the unusual or powerful events which are most critical; sometimes what is ordinary becomes extraordinary by its interpretation, representation or articulation.

Critical reflection and careful analysis of caring moments thus transformed into critical incidents can enhance learning and inform practice. An important feature of the transformatory nature of reflection on these incidents is the scientific and/or professional knowledge and understanding which are brought to bear in one's thinking. However, Ghaye (1997, p. 80) notes that Minghella and Benson claim that:

... most incidents appear to represent inter-personal or interactional situations rather than clinical procedural problems.

Tripp (1993, p. 98), too, recognises the affective emphasis of most incidents:

The high emotional charge ensures that the incidents always remain with us in spite of everything else we experience over the years. We cringe or stand tall when we touch them in memory.

Caring moments are those instants in time and place which are a distillation of quality care and genuine humanity. They are critical incidents which embody professional and/or personal merit and offer much in the way of encapsulating the elements of good practice. The act of reflecting on the caring moment described in the story above transforms it into a 'lived metaphor' (Ghaye, 1997) from which much can be learned.

Critical reflection on the caring moment illustrated in this story exposes practice which correlates with Bronfenbrenner's (1979) 'ecological perspective' in the care of others. He expressed the view that children should not be perceived in isolated contexts. Every child is a 'home child' and a 'community child' as well as a 'school child'. Events, feelings and values are inextricably bound up within the complex context of the learning. Learning does not take place in isolated contexts – it is dependent on the interaction of the individual's 'whole life' experiences. The wise professional is one who not only acknowledges the 'whole' person but who capitalises on such knowledge to bring about improvements in condition.

A participant's perspective

We was really surprised when we went into the classroom 'cos Rachel was crying and Mrs Taylor went over and asked her what's the matter. Kevin didn't hear what she said but I did, and I told him that her cat's dead. Then Rebecca came in and she started crying as well, and Miss gave them both a cuddle, but they was still crying, so then we all went and sat in the 'comfy corner'.

Mrs Taylor's always really kind and she helps you. She was talking about the cat and all the stuff he used to do, and we told her all about our pets, too, and Dave said he even had a Grandma wot died (but he always makes things up, so I don't really believe him). And then I remembered my guinea pig. He was called 'Shilling', and my mum said that was supposed to be a joke or something. Anyway, he died ages ago and I was really sad. I cried a lot when Mum found him dead in his cage, and we didn't know why he was dead or anything!

And when we was sitting in the comfy corner I remembered him, and it made me feel kind of funny, and then I felt sorry for Rebecca and Rachel 'cos their cat had died.

A caring moment may appear very differently to each of those who were present when it occurred. Reality is an interpretation of the world from an individual's perspective. Thus, when examining the same caring moment from the different viewpoints of an observer, an insider, and a participant observer, the interpretation of the event and certainly the emphases will not necessarily be the same. In relation to the incident recounted, in the practitioner's mind this was not an exceptional event but nonetheless one which needed sensitive management and, in the short term, was appreciated as significant for further reflection.

In the participant observer's view (my view) the defined caring moment was wholly un-noteworthy, since this kind of caring behaviour was what the children had learned to expect from their teacher. For Wayne, though, the whole incident determined a significant point in his interpersonal development, marked by his realisation that he was truly able to relate to how another child was feeling.

A caring moment is not an accident of good fortune; it is action underpinned by the practitioner's sound knowledge, skills and understanding of their chosen field. Within any professional context, the basic human needs of the client group (such as sufficient heat, light, and physical comfort) are, of course, vitally important (Maslow, 1970), and a basic level of professional competencies which includes a positive commitment and an ability to relate to and to motivate others are also of fundamental importance. All of these competencies must harmonise with the institutional policies, custom and practice. Caring moments are those incidents that tie policy, practice, the organisation and the individual together in that they are underpinned by competence and theory but are also supplemented by sound personal values and principles.

In discussing Mrs Taylor's management of the incident, I identified a tension in her professional duties. At one level she felt legally obliged to her job (to deliver the curriculum) – after all, she was paid to carry out her duties as identified in her contract – but, at a deeper level, she was experienced enough to realise that the identified primary duties were superseded by her wider professional commitment to the well-being of her other charges – she acted as she did, not just out of common human decency, but from a professional understanding of the needs of those in her care.

That said, she needed to feel confident and justified in her choices, since she remained answerable to her employers. It was imperative that she would be able to offer a valid defence of her professional decision, if necessary, in order to justify her practice (for example, to an inspection by anyone in authority).

She demonstrated a proficient knowledge and understanding of her professional context and, in her sensitive management of the situation, achieved a successful and beneficial outcome for all concerned. She acted in accordance with the holistic needs of those in her care. This 'emotional intelligence' (Goleman, 1995) is a hallmark of effectiveness for those in the caring professions.

In dealing with the incident in a caring and emotionally sensitive way, she also displayed the quality of flexibility. She was sufficiently confident and knowledgeable in her practice to digress appropriately to the needs of those in her care. As professionals gain experience and expertise, they develop more choices in their practice, but this extended toolkit means that they also need to develop sophisticated skills in choosing appropriately. Though skilled and intelligent practice can become automatic (judicious choices being made at an almost instinctive level), it is necessary to guard against complacency, which frequency and/or habit can precipitate.

It has been suggested that professionals should aim to move through a learning process, progressing from unconscious incompetence, through conscious incompetence and conscious competence, to unconscious competence. However, it may be argued that action researchers in healthcare and allied professions might believe that the state of unconscious competence is a somewhat smug and static condition. To be an effective action researcher requires dedicated critical reflection on practice – continual and systematic review of negated values which leads to action for improvements to practice.

The originator of the caring moment told here showed keen powers of observation and a detailed knowledge of those in her care. She was able to prioritise needs and draw on her substantial professional experience and expertise in order to manage the situation successfully.

This practitioner also recognised the importance of individual perceptions. She understood that what might appear a somewhat trivial occurrence was, to Rachel and Rebecca, a traumatic and life-changing episode. Everyone has a different life map, his or her own individual version of reality. Reality may be regarded as multifaceted, multi-layered and existing differentially for each individual. Such sensitivity to the perceptions of others is another feature of emotional intelligence; the ability to see things from another's perspective fosters positive relationships.

> For men and women are not only themselves; they are the region in which they were born, the city, apartment or farm in which they learned to walk, the old wives tales they overheard, the food they ate, the schools they attended, the sports they followed, the poems they read, and the God they believed in. (Somerset Maugham, 1945)

When critical incidents such as these 'caring moments' are shared with colleagues, the professional dialogue that ensues can be transformative for all concerned. Practice may be evaluated against criteria which indicate good clinical and professional care. When an individual practitioner examines a phenomenon, it is like a single beam of light shining on an object from one direction, illuminating just one aspect of the phenomenon; but a group of practitioners focusing their collective professional body of knowledge and different experiences on a phenomenon is akin to focusing a number of intense, powerful beams of light on an object from a variety of directions. In this way, the object is illuminated from all angles, and a more informed view and a better understanding can result.

So it may be seen that professional discourse on caring moments can highlight good practice and questions should be asked of the kind:

- What have I learned from that experience?
- What, in that situation, was well managed? In what way?
- How might that situation have been better managed?
- How far did I live my values out in my professional practice here?
- How did others in the situation feel?
- What implications are there for future practice for me? For others?
- Was I able to meet the demands of my job?
- Was there a conflict between the demands of the job and my personal value system?

These questions fit within the spiralling cycle of professional practice identified by Ghaye *et al.* (1997, p. 34). Answers to questions such as these allow the reconstruction of theory–practice relationships that inform future improvement. Examining one's responses in the workplace in relation to others allows both subjective and objective evaluation of practice. In making claims for improvement, one can utilise the analysis as evidence of one's increasing competence, not just in professional practice, but in one's level of reflective practice too.

From this professional dialogue between peers it then becomes possible, at the highest levels, to synthesise individual and collective improvements with systemic and cultural improvements in the organisation; to identify and evaluate links between enhanced professionalism and empowered carers; and to generalise from specific examples to the more global issues for care.

In summary, consideration of caring moments has much to offer the practitioner, both on an individual level and as part of a team. In reflecting on the elements of good practice exemplified in a caring moment, generic competencies can be identified which may inform the practice of others.

In Mrs Taylor's case these competencies included a detailed knowledge of her chosen field, a sound theoretical knowledge base, wisdom, keen powers of observation, skill, commitment, an ability to motivate others, and sensitive understanding of those for whom she had responsibility. She also demonstrated a clear understanding of the essential consideration of individual differences, not just in terms of individual needs, but also in terms of sensitivity to people's individual perceptions; she exhibited confidence in her choice of action, exercised emotional intelligence in her decision-making, and demonstrated dedication to her espoused values and principles.

In reflecting on her own caring moment (in this case captured by me, a participant observer), Mrs Taylor will continue to find ways to improve her practice; sharing the event and the process of reflection with others will enhance their professional practice too. Sharing and discussing caring moments increases our ability to identify and learn from other such incidents. We are enabled to recognise these events which embody good practice and compassion. Our ability to discern such incidents is enhanced so that these caring moments – shining examples of humanity – appear as if randomly scattered throughout our working life, and, like finding the rainbows made by oil in puddles, we can continue to be surprised and delighted at finding goodness where we sometimes least expect it.

References

Bronfenbrenner, U. (1979) *The Ecology of Human Development*. Harvard University Press, Cambridge, MA.

Chapman, V. (1998) Moving experiences: the integration of a neuropsychological approach with parental perceptions in developing an understanding of developmental co-ordination disorder. *Unpublished Doctoral Dissertation*, University of Coventry.

Ghaye, A. (1997) Some reflections on the nature of educational action research. *School Libraries World-wide*, 3(2), 1–10.

Ghaye, T. *et al.* (1997) *Learning through Critical Reflective Practice: An Introduction*. Pentaxion Press, Newcastle upon Tyne.

Goleman, D. (1995) *Emotional Intelligence – Why It Can Matter More Than I.Q.* Bloomsbury, London.

Maslow, A. H. (1970) *Motivation and Personality*. Harper & Row, London.

Somerset Maugham, W. (1945) *The Razor's Edge*. Reprint Society, London.

Tripp, D. (1993) *Critical Incidents in Teaching*. Routledge, London.

CHAPTER 8

A caring moment
with Ann

Sarah Mann and Tony Ghaye

According to Burnard (1991), all practitioners need to improve practice and find better ways to care for patients. Through this chapter I will draw upon a 'caring moment', which I will also call an 'incident', that occurred early in my nursing career and use Gibbs' (1988) reflective cycle to demonstrate how practice can be interrogated and learned from through systematic and repeated reflections.

I (Sarah – see p. 81) work in an endoscopy unit which forms part of a larger day surgery unit. There are a variety of investigations carried out within the unit including, gastroscopies, sigmoidoscopies, colonoscopies and bronchoscopies. In recent years improvements in technology have meant that the investigations are relatively quick and painless, although they remain uncomfortable, for the patient. Due to these improvements in procedures and the fast turnover of patients, the skills required by the nurses within this unit differ from their peers on wards or within the community setting. These skills specifically relate to the reduced period of time allowed for building a rapport or relationship with the patient. Skills of assessment are also important to the nurse within this area, as patients' physical, psychological and emotional needs must be assessed in a short period in order to deliver a high quality of nursing care. The nurse must also be competent in the admission of patients, recovering patients from the sedation following the investigation and discharging the patient home or back to the ward. It is relevant to note that the majority of patients are informed of the investigation results prior to leaving the unit, this may involve giving the patient a serious diagnosis.

Using Gibbs' (1988) model of reflection I have been able to reflect on and analyse the following incident in a positive manner. This model is often drawn as a cycle and is shown in Figure 8.1.

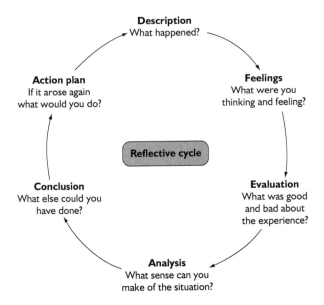

Figure 8.1 Model of reflection (Gibbs, 1988).

Describing the incident

Gibbs notes that the first part of the reflective cycle is to describe the incident or caring moment. Such a moment occurred during my first week in this post in the endoscopy unit at this hospital and has remained with me for the past two years.

Ann was, like most patients, attending the endoscopy unit. It was her first visit and she was accompanied by her husband. She appeared apprehensive; however, she attempted to hide her fears. Her assessment revealed a history of bowel problems. I was able to explain to her what she could expect to feel, although she would be sedated through the procedure, and that she would be given some idea of her diagnosis before she left the department. A rapport was soon established and Ann talked about her planned visit to see her daughter in America and the plans she had for her early retirement from work.

Ann's colonoscopy was abandoned part way into the procedure due to her discomfort. She had, however, no recollection of this following the procedure, as she had been sedated. I was then to care for her during her recovery period. A barium enema followed the procedure to confirm a diagnosis. This had not been planned, so the procedure was explained to Ann and reasons given.

Following the barium enema I accompanied Ann and her husband while they talked to the consultant about the diagnosis. Ann was informed by the consultant that a carcinoma of the caecum had been identified and that she would require surgery the following week. This would result in a permanent colostomy.

Describing my feelings

Reflecting on this situation has allowed me to analyse my feelings and my concern about my own lack of skills at the time, i.e. of letting the patient down, of being in too much of a hurry to get on with the next task, of not knowing what to say and therefore avoiding saying too much. Nurses' training does not cover in great detail the communication needed when dealing with seriously ill patients (Walsh and Ford, 1990) and, as a newly qualified practitioner, I felt inadequate to do this competently and confidently.

As expected, when being informed of such news, Ann's reaction was one of shock. In the space of one morning her plans had been turned around and her world had collapsed. The consultant explained that although the diagnosis was bad, the prognosis was good, as they had discovered the growth in its early stages. It was at this stage that Ann wanted to know what to do next. I did not know. I did not know who to contact to seek advice for her or how the hospital procedures worked. An appointment was made for a visit in three days to see the consultant, allowing her time to reflect on the information she had received. My inadequacies, I felt, were that I had not done anything for this patient. She had left the department and I continued with the next patient. Reflecting on this incident two years later, I still feel inadequate and guilty, as I was not able to help in a constructive manner or offer comfort to Ann at the time in the way that I felt I should.

Evaluating

Ann was instantly likeable. She was easy to talk to and forthcoming with information. I felt that the preparation for the procedure had been completed and the care was of an appropriate standard. It was the telling of the information to Ann that had the most bearing on my feelings. I was also shocked at the results. I was upset for Ann and her family and felt my own inadequacies in offering practical advice or help in this situation. I was angry with the consultant for not telling me the diagnosis before consulting with the patient and allowing me to come to terms with the news for myself before assisting the patient. I was also angry with myself for not asking him what the diagnosis was. Such anger and wanting to direct it at someone is a natural reaction. The consultant's main concern was for Ann in wanting to tell her the diagnosis as soon as possible.

On reflection, I am not sure if he felt I was there to support him or Ann. I now feel that communication could have been better between ourselves as members of a multidisciplinary team in the provision of care. In trying to evaluate or to make sense of this 'moment' I think that few good things came out of this experience. From Ann's point of view she did have an early diagnosis, but what of her psychological and emotional care? From the departmental point of view it could be deemed a success. The patient attended, was treated, diagnosis made and curative surgery planned. This perception leaves me feeling cold, and questioning whether we did care for the patient in a holistic manner. Are we seeing patients as whole, or just as 'the colonoscopy in cubical four'? I felt that while Ann's physical needs had been met, her psychological and emotional needs were neglected.

Analysing the incident

In order to ensure that these other needs are met, time should be taken with the patient. It is quick and easy to give someone the facts but treating them as a whole person takes longer. There are a great many issues relating to this incident. My values of nursing were being challenged. I needed to support this patient while coming to terms with the information myself. My ethical knowledge (Carper, 1978), which deals with the moral code that we hold as individuals, was being compromised. I knew we needed time and that my silence in the circumstances was due to my own inadequacies. The scientific knowledge that should have been taught within the theoretical part of my training did not correspond with the practice that I was now experiencing. My beliefs in patient care were also not being played out in relation to the support that I could have found for this person as I was unaware of the facilities within the hospital at this time.

Conclusion and action plan

Reflection, according to Jay (1995), heightens self-awareness and enables the individual to gain an increased understanding of the effects that past experiences have on care delivery. This is certainly true as I reflect on this incident. Several issues concerning my own theory/practice knowledge gap and the care of future patients were identified. Gaps in personal knowledge were also identified by this incident. For example, I later found out that the hospital has a stoma nurse and contact names could have been given. This highlights the issue of new staff and how they are inducted within the unit and hospital. There is a need to give new staff a broader organisational picture so that they can use this information with their patients if necessary.

Using the Gibbs model helps me to think beyond my initial feelings and identify; the strengths and limitations of my own knowledge, procedures that could be improved, and the holistic manner which we, as healthcare professionals, need to address the patient. As I reflected on my practice in this kind of systematic manner, I have learned that the finding out of information and the communication skills required when informing patients of bad news are areas that I have to address. The reflective process has given me the clarity of thinking and incentive to do something about this. I now feel in a position to assist others. The action plan following this reflection includes the gaining of new skills, changing of unit policy in relation to the induction of staff and the improvement of patient care in relation to their psychological and emotional needs.

Reflecting on my reflections some time later with my colleague Tony

(*The remainder of this chapter was co-written with Tony.*)

In continuing to think about this caring moment with Ann some time later, in discussion with Tony, I feel that there is much more that I have learned. What follows is therefore my attempt at a kind of meta-reflection. That is to say, I want to enter the final part of this chapter by 'thinking again' (Clandinin and Connelly, 1995) about what I learned, or think I have learned! I wish to claim that I have learned that there are many ways to reflect on my practice. At the time I opted to use a reflective process that is most appropriately described as a 'cycle'. This seemed comfortable and natural. It resonated nicely with 'where I was at' in my own professional development at that time. Ghaye and Lillyman (2006) point out that cycles have an unfinished business feel to them. They argue that out of the stopping point called an 'action plan' come new clinical and managerial actions, encounters and situations. These can be understood more deeply and richly by asking again the first of Gibbs' questions, namely, 'What happened?'.

I think I really began this learning cycle in the way suggested by Atkins and Murphy (1994). That is to say, with an awareness of uncomfortable feelings and thoughts. I now appreciate that this is only one of many starting points. We often begin with the things that went less well or the things that we feel inadequate about in some way. Reflection-on-practice is not just an exercise in remedial action. It is not just about putting something 'right', even if this is known and possible in some way. I still feel that reflective cycles or spirals are useful to busy practitioners. They can help the individual. They are relatively uncomplicated to understand and therefore not too off-putting. Perhaps the most important thing is that they convey a clear message that learning is a lifelong business. It is a continuous developing process dependent upon active reflection and reflective action (Ghaye and Lillyman, 2010). But I have also learned that no one 'model' can do it all. Each has limitations. The one I used and present here does not really help me to reveal the importance of my nursing values in trying to make sense of practice. It does not lead me into thinking about the powerful organisational culture that serves to help or stifle my practice. These frameworks are useful if used wisely. We should avoid becoming enslaved by them. Structured reflection makes good sense but can be enriched if done collaboratively, more publicly and, for example, with adequate support. Ghaye and Ghaye (1998) suggest that irrespective of any kind of model of reflection, improving practice through reflection requires us to:

1. *Problematise what we do*: In essence this is about reflecting on what is happening and why and linking this to what our intentions are and why we hold them.
2. *Create a 'text'*: This means we have to reflect on something. A 'text' or record of what has happened is the starting point. The text is the evidential base, derived from practice, that is our raw material to work upon.
3. *Confront yourself/ourselves*: They suggest that questioning practice is the key process here. The challenging thing is to come up with answers to what questions, asked by whom, when?
4. *Refocus and be creative*: The big issue here is that reflection needs to have a consequence. Through questioning what we do, with confidence and support, we give ourselves a chance to open up new possibilities and new directions for improved healthcare action.

In more general terms my reflections on this 'caring moment' with Ann have led me to understand that reflecting on practice is more than just reflecting in some speculative way. It implies a commitment to at least try to improve what I/we think and do in the unit, our local policies and, if possible and appropriate, improve the 'system' within which practice is embedded and policy is generated. For most practitioners, trying to tackle the system might be envisaged, but it would be a massive step to try to follow this through. A duty of care and a commitment to continuously improve client care is a moral commitment. Together these things begin to say something about the nature of being a reflective practitioner. Eraut (1993) is helpful in this respect as his work enables me to appreciate that this can be seen in relation to:

■ a moral commitment to try to serve the interests of my clients/patients by reflecting on their well-being and their progress and by making decisions about how care can most appropriately be enhanced

- a professional obligation to review the nature of my clinical work and the effectiveness of what I do (as well as others) in order to continuously try to improve the quality of care
- a professional obligation to continue to develop my practical nursing knowledge both by personal reflection on practice and through my interactions with others

This caring moment with Ann has served as a catalyst for other kinds of learning. For example, it has taught me that reflection is indeed a process of turning experience into learning:

> It is not idle meanderings or day-dreaming, but purposive activity directed towards a goal. (Boud *et al.*, 1998, p. 11)

Apart from the important goal of striving to improve practice, there are other goals. For me, now, another one is to use reflection to help me to maintain safe and accountable practice in a rapidly transforming healthcare service (Department of Health, 1998). To complicate things further, our society is also changing rapidly. One consequence of this is that we are faced with an increasing chaos of choice, social and professional identity. Some features of this age are instability, complexity, transience and lack of conformity. Given this general scenario, healthcare professionals need support and guidance in trying to make sense of and survive these unstable and unpredictable clinical contexts. The healthcare professional in the twenty-first century will need to be flexible, responsive and creative at work. I have learned that the core to being creative is a willingness to reflect critically on practice and to adapt plans and practice accordingly (Craft, 1997).

One last point. In reflecting again on my caring moment with Ann, I have come to understand more clearly how 'reflection-on-practice' is not simply about 'learning from experience' in some neat, tidy, safe and cosy manner. The two phrases are not synonymous. There is a difference that makes a difference. To learn from experience we need to give experience meaning in some way. Understanding does not come from my experience alone. Understanding experience and having an opportunity to learn from it requires, for me anyway, some set of principles and processes that help to make sense of practice. This is the role of reflection. Reflection is not just linked to a notion of learning that is cumulative and incremental. In other words, as we get more experienced in practice we get more ideas, more knowledge and more skills. This is joining reflection with an idea of learning as a quantity. This is a very limiting and skewed view of reflection. Reflection is fundamentally about a conception of learning that is to do with the quality of our perceptions and how we see things. Achieving this can be uncomfortable and feel from time to time anything but cumulative and incremental. The reflective process often requires us to 'unlearn'. This does not mean to forget. It means to unravel the complex whole of clinical practice and try to knit it all up again. It is in this process of reconstruction that we might see further, deeper and more clearly and, in doing so, come to know what is indeed a caring moment.

References

Atkins, S. and Murphy, K. (1994) Reflective practice. *Nursing Standard*, **8**(39), 49–56.

Boud, D., Keogh, R. and Walker, D. (eds.) (1998) *Reflection: Turning Experience into Learning*. Kogan Page, London.

Burnard, P. (1991) Improving through reflection. *Journal of District Nursing*, May, 10–12.

Carper, B. (1978) Fundamental patterns of knowing in nursing. *Advances in Nursing Science*, **1**(1), 13–23.

Clandinin, J. and Connelly, M. (1995) *Teacher's Professional Knowledge Landscapes*. Teacher's College Press, New York.

Craft, A. (1997) Identity and creativity: educating teachers for postmodernism? *Teacher Development*, **1**(1), 83–96.

Department of Health (1998) *A First Class Service: Quality in the New NHS*. HMSO, London.

Eraut, M. (1993) *Developing Professional Knowledge within a Client-centred Orientation*. Unpublished paper, University of Sussex.

Ghaye, T. and Ghaye, K. (1998) *Teaching and Learning through Critical Reflective Practice*. David Fulton Publishers, London.

Ghaye, T. and Lillyman, S. (2006) *Learning Journals and Critical Incidents: Reflective Practice for Healthcare Professionals*, 2nd edn. Quay Books, London.

Ghaye, T. and Lillyman, S. (2010) *Reflection: Principles and Practice for Healthcare Professionals* (2nd edn). Quay Books, London.

Gibbs, G. (1988) *Learning by Doing: A Guide to Teaching and Learning Methods*. Further Education Unit, Oxford Brookes University, Oxford.

Jay, T. (1995) The use of reflection to enhance practice. *Professional Nurse*, **10**(9), 593–6.

Walsh, M. and Ford, P. (1990) *Nursing Rituals: Research and Rational Actions*. Heinemann Nursing, Oxford.

CHAPTER 9

A caring moment with Margaret

Helen Taylor

The caring moment

My previous encounters with Margaret had been brief. I had dashed in and out of her room on many occasions. I would hand her first her pills, and then a glass of water poured from the jug on the table beside her chair. Usually I would stand as she took each tablet individually, gulping mouthfuls of water to swill them down. I would often ask the same questions: 'How are you today?' 'Do you want your curtains opened?' And then make an appropriate comment on the weather 'Oh, it's a lovely/sunny/windy/wet/frosty day today'. I would then take the glass from her hand, replace it on the table, and repeat the process with the resident in the next room. The drug rounds were large and took a long time. Some of the residents had problems swallowing. Others were confused and could easily become frightened or aggressive if they were not treated with the utmost care.

I was working as an RN in a large nursing home. On the morning shift I would have charge of one of the two floors, 22 residents and three care assistants. On an afternoon shift I would have sole charge of the entire home of 44 residents and six care assistants. I was always very busy. 'I'll come back later' and 'Someone will be along to help you in a moment' were oft-repeated phrases as I dashed around changing dressings, administering drugs and checking on residents that care assistants had expressed concern about. I spent time with relatives, answering telephone queries and assessing residents that had fallen. I had a responsibility for the total care of some very elderly, dependent and vulnerable people.

These people were not in hospital; this was their home. Some of them had been resident for many years. We celebrated their birthdays and mourned their deaths. In many cases we became closely involved with their families. They shared news of births and exam successes, but we avoided involvement in the inevitable arguments and disputes. Relatives often experienced feelings of guilt. They felt that putting their parent in a home was the ultimate act of betrayal. These sons or daughters needed a lot of reassurance and support. They usually coped by spending as much time as possible with their parent, and could be very critical of the care they received. The work was very emotionally and physically demanding. Margaret had been resident for two years, admitted because she was no longer able to cope at home. She suffered from chronic depression, and had also had a C.V.A. several years previously which had left her with a left-sided weakness. She was no longer able to walk, even aided.

On several occasions I had been called to Margaret's room because she had been discovered lying on the floor. It was generally accepted that Margaret placed herself on the floor deliberately, sometimes with quite devastating results. On a number of occasions she had been witnessed easing her body from the chair, pushing the table out of the way beforehand. Despite receiving psychiatric support and anti-depressants, Margaret continued to inflict sometimes serious injuries on herself. This was something the staff found difficult to cope with.

Some of the care assistants considered her to be 'bell-happy'. Each time a resident rang their nurse call bell it was logged by a computerised system. On a number of occasions Margaret had been found to ring her bell in excess of 50 times in a six-hour period. On days such as these, the staff would lose patience with her. Often when asked how they could help her, Margaret would either not reply or say that she did not know. It was difficult to know how to help.

On this particular morning, I had given Margaret her morning pills as I had many times before. We were, as usual, extremely busy. One of the agency staff had not arrived for her shift. After I had completed the drug round, I fed Mary a bowl of porridge and a cup of tea. The residents had breakfast in their own rooms, so we dashed around collecting the trays. I collected Margaret's. The night shift often dressed her, but on this occasion they had not. She was sitting in an upright armchair facing out into the corridor, a thick, pink velour dressing gown draped around her shoulders. Her thin face was a mass of bruises, scars and scabs. I knew that her arms and legs had a similar appearance. She looked at me. She had cornflakes encrusted around her mouth, and tea had dribbled down her chin. More cornflakes were littered on the table and on her clothes. 'Please Sister', she pleaded. 'I'm wet.'

At this point I looked at the photographs on her chest of drawers. I had seen them many times, but this time a familiar face grabbed my attention. Familiar, but not the same. Beautifully styled hair, impeccably applied cosmetics. No cornflakes, tea, bruises scabs or scars. This was a face full of joy and optimism, gazing into the eyes of a man she obviously loved very much. Not the face full of humiliation and despair before me now. I put down the tray that I was holding and put my arms around her shoulders. I experienced a feeling of deep warmth for this deeply unhappy lady. She seemed to enjoy the contact. I asked her if she would like a bath. She nodded. I assured Margaret that I would be back very soon. I gave my staff a hurried report on any changes to the residents' conditions overnight, and then made allocations. Although there was a named nurse system, it was often impossible to operationalise because of staff shortages and turnover. Within five minutes people were scurrying in all directions, collecting the last of the trays and then going to prepare the residents for the day.

I hurried back to Margaret's room, having started to run a bath on the way. I knocked on the closed door and entered. I transferred her into a wheelchair and then positioned her in front of the wardrobe. I opened the door. 'What would you like to wear today?', I asked. She looked at me mutely. 'OK then, would you like trousers or a skirt?' 'Skirt', she answered. I then hunted through the wardrobe until Margaret had selected her outfit, a pleated beige skirt and a cream, lace trimmed blouse. She opted to take a beige cardigan with us to the bathroom, and decide then whether to wear it or not. Margaret was not enthusiastic when I asked if she wanted to take any toiletries, but I took some anyway.

In the bathroom she agreed to having some bubble bath put in the water. As the room filled with steam and the bath filled with rose scented foam, I gently peeled off her urine soaked clothes. They didn't come', she said 'I asked them but they didn't come'. I bent and looked into her eyes, once bright and clear, now opaque with cataracts, and blurred with tears. 'I am sorry', I said. I really was. I helped her onto the toilet, and giving her the bell cord, went to wait outside. Everywhere around me there was activity. The domestic vented some frustration on the carpet as she hoovered. Care assistants rushed around with arms full of towels. Bells rang. An unmistakable smell of urine escaped from some of the rooms. The bell rang. I knocked and went back into the bathroom.

I tested the temperature of the water before I helped Margaret into the bath. It felt fine, but she asked for a little more cold to be added. I did so, and then asked her to hold on to the handles while I reclined the Parker bath. Once she had adjusted to the sensation of the warm water covering her body, Margaret visibly seemed to relax. I asked her if she would like the whirlpool on. She nodded. Not all of the residents like the sensation of the water bubbling around them, but most seem to find it very soothing. I gave Margaret a cloth and held the soap for her, and she began to wash, careful not to knock off the scabs. Such gentleness seemed to be at odds with the fact that she had inflicted those injuries on herself. I sat on a chair next to the bath. I asked her if she had ever worked. In a quiet, stuttering voice she told me about the Second World War. She had been a nurse and had worked overseas with the forces. I was surprised as there was no mention of this in her notes and no one had told me that Margaret had been a nurse. All the time she was talking, she stared into my eyes. I was close enough for her to see. Sometimes this can feel uncomfortable, disconcerting, but I felt that Margaret needed to know that I was really listening.

Margaret had met her husband towards the end of the war. He had been widowed and left with three young children. He had wooed her and whisked her off her feet. He was the love of her life. They were wealthy and lived a comfortable life. She became stepmother to his children. They had resented her, and never fully accepted her. At this point, I recalled a rather anxious-looking middle aged woman that came to visit Margaret most weekends. She seemed to care and always showed an interest in how Margaret was. I asked Margaret about her. She told me that she was her stepdaughter and that they had got on quite well. Her two stepsons, however, had never really seemed to like her. Margaret's big regret was that she had never had children of her own. She had tried to love her husband's children as her own. He had not wanted any more. Her husband had had a fatal heart attack almost 20 years ago. The children had left home and Margaret was alone. She had a lot of friends, she told me, but it was not the same.

'I'm getting cold', said Margaret. I finished washing her feet, and then raised the bath back into an upright position. I wrapped her battered body in warm, fluffy towels. She looked sad, and I felt sad that a person should feel so much pain that they could inflict even more on themselves. I gently dried her and dressed her. She agreed to have some perfume and lipstick on, and decided that she would have her cardigan on. I handed her the comb. She was careful not to disturb the scabs on her scalp. I gathered her things together and wheeled her back into her room, the scent of roses following us up the corridor. After I had settled her into her chair she asked me to put the radio on. She could not read any more, she told me. She was waiting to have her cataracts removed. She greatly enjoyed reading and missed it. How did she fill her day? Before I left the room, I stood back and looked at her. She looked comfortable in her chair, with a rug tucked around her legs. Her bed was made, the room was tidy and the early spring sunlight glistened on an exquisite crystal vase full of daffodils in the window. The light and the lipstick made her face come alive. I told her that she looked lovely, and she smiled. I meant it; she was a beautiful woman.

Some of my reflections on this caring moment

I reflected on this caring moment during my coffee break later that morning, intuitively drawing upon my understanding of reflection. Initially, I simply felt satisfaction that I had helped to make Margaret physically comfortable. I had spent time with her, listened to her and treated her with respect and helped to maintain her dignity. I felt that I had 'connected' with her, developed an understanding of who and what she was. This 85-year-old lady had led a full life before she became old and dependent upon others for almost every aspect of living. She was educated and had travelled and experienced the world. She had loved and been loved.

This interaction has had a significant effect on my professional practice and on me personally. Why? I had worked in several nursing homes and had worked with many elderly people. I remember most of them, but I believe that Margaret has had the greatest impact on me. I have thought about that time we spent together many times, wondering if I had really helped her, what I had done well and how I could have helped her more. Margaret made me acknowledge and confront theories and ideologies, challenge my own approach to nursing and how I teach junior staff. It helped me to clarify expectations of myself and others.

Holistic care had been the main ethos of my undergraduate nurse training, and I had thought that I had incorporated it into my professional practice. I wanted to know my residents, to understand them. When caring for the elderly I attempt to remember that the small, wasted being that I am feeding is an individual who has experienced far more life than I have. They have lived through a war, maybe two. They have cooked meals, managed budgets, planted vegetables and perhaps given birth. They have known pain and hardship, joy and triumph. They have splashed through puddles in the rain and slipped on ice. I felt ashamed that for a long time with Margaret I had not really seen this. I had spent time with her in the past, but she had been unresponsive to me. Unfortunately, I allowed this to shape my perception of her. Why had it been a surprise to me that she had been a nurse, was well travelled and educated? Possibly because I was afraid of the commitment of getting to know her and why she was in so much emotional pain. I used the excuse of being too busy because if I knew the truth then I would have to deal with it.

Gibson (1994) suggested that by 'allowing' an older person to reminisce, a carer is reversing roles. They are receiving a gift of knowledge from a person who is used to being the recipient of care. This may help improve the older person's feeling of self-worth. By discussing their past they are reviewing their life. This may help to put their current situation into perspective. I was pleased that Margaret felt able to talk to me. I have talked to her again about her nursing career. It is terrible to think about the wealth of knowledge and experience that dies when a person does. I encourage care assistants to talk to the residents. They have made some quite surprising discoveries.

When I had told the care assistants that I would be bathing Margaret that morning they had said 'good'. She was not a popular resident. I must confess that I would not usually have volunteered to dress her. Her physical appearance was threatening, evidence of our failure to help her. She was demanding and needy.

Staff responses to Margaret may be considered in the context of Stockwell's (1972) definition of the 'unpopular patient'. She proposed that individuals operating within a discrete situation may be considered to be a 'group' and that, as such, the members would be bound by 'laws that govern the behaviour of people in small social groups'. These are either implicit or explicit. Those members of the group who do not conform to these laws or rules, for whatever reason, will be considered by the others to be 'deviant'. Deviance will almost invariably result in the offending individual becoming unpopular with other group members. Residents and staff may be considered members of a group. They are living and working in the same organisation. Rules are essential for the effective operation of this organisation.

Some of the care assistants thought that Margaret was selfish: dominating their time. When she rang her bell they would often have to leave the resident they were with to attend to her. She was breaking the rules. This frustrated them – they wanted to provide good care to all the residents, not just the demanding few. I thought about my own responses to Margaret in the past. If called to her after she had fallen I would be worried that she had hurt herself. I would check her for fractures, cuts and bruising. I would talk to her, ask why she had done it. Did I really want to know? I would attempt to comfort her. But, at the back of my mind would be the thought that I now had a lot of paperwork to complete: accident forms and so on. I would sense the irritation of the care assistants as they stood behind me, hands on hips. They may have had to interrupt feeding someone to tend, yet again, to Margaret. This illustrates the point, made by Millar (1990), that perceptions of what is difficult or deviant behaviour are subjective, often dependent on the situation within which the behaviour occurs and who is involved. When staff were less busy Margaret was more likely to be treated sympathetically. Some staff were naturally more inclined to empathise with Margaret than others.

Ferry (1994) reported on an operant/respondent hypothesis, that in some individuals depression may lead to self-harm, and that the harm would reduce for a time the feeling of depression. The cycle is therefore self-reinforcing. At times of depression the person will self-harm. The greater the depression, the greater the physical harm. A physical pain to alleviate an emotional pain. A positive feedback mechanism. An awareness of what they are doing to themselves physically, may well make the individual feel more wretched, it certainly will not make them feel better. Although my words were sympathetic, I am sure that if Margaret had been aware of our negative body language, it cannot have helped resolve her emotional pain.

Murray (1998) suggested that there is often little nurses can do to prevent self-harm. The individual needs support and people to understand that they are harming themselves to cope with their distress. He proposed that to understand their suffering, care givers should not suppress their subjectivity. They must not, however, be judgmental, either verbally or non-verbally. Harrison (1998) stated that these people need understanding and empathy, and should not be dismissed as manipulative. We need to examine our own attitudes and prejudices. During that time in the bathroom with Margaret, we were able to communicate effectively. I saw, in part, why she was so unhappy. She felt that her life was empty, sad and lonely. The anti-depressants did not take that emotional pain away. Nothing could, but perhaps some empathetic support would make her feel a little less alone, more valued as a person. One can only imagine how it feels to go from being independent and self-determining to being wholly dependent on strangers for everything. Margaret is continent but unable to walk. In order to get to the toilet she needed someone to respond to her call bell. Sometimes, if staff were busy, she would wait and wait, and then perhaps wet herself. This upsets me. It is difficult to acknowledge that a person who has full bladder control may have incontinence imposed upon them.

Allen (1996) described the distressing situation a hospitalised elderly relative found herself in. She had requested to use the bedpan at mealtime, only to be told that she would have to wait until the meal was over because of the risk of cross-infection. On a couple of occasions this poor lady had wet the bed. She experienced a feeling of great embarrassment. I am sure that all nurses can recall an occasion when they have asked someone to wait 'just a moment'. I can. Imagine how you would feel if you were sitting in a lecture, for example, and were forbidden to leave the room after having been given a large dose of diuretics. You tried to control it, but could not, and wet yourself.

A study by Patterson (1995) investigated the process of residents settling into nursing home life. Moving away from familiar surroundings into what is essentially an institutional setting is a very stressful experience. Patterson examined new residents' perceptions of what staff behaviours they considered to be supportive and non-supportive. Physical assistance, such as being helped into the bath and having call bells responded to promptly rated highly on the supportive behaviours.

A lack of sympathy for the effects of ageing, a display of negative attitudes to the resident, and a failure for staff to show concern or respect were identified as non-supportive.

If we have needs it is easier to cope with them if they are dealt with efficiently. Imagine if you had gone to a restaurant for a meal. You had to stand, awkwardly, for five minutes before you could attract a waiter's attention. You were then seated and left. You had no cutlery. No one offered you a drink. Again you had to try to attract the waiter's attention. 'OK, OK', he said, and stood shuffling from one foot to the other while you attempted to order your food. It arrived after rather a long wait. The waiter disappeared before you could remind him that you had no cutlery. You would probably feel very uncomfortable about summoning this unhelpful character again. By the time you got to eat your meal it was cold. If you were assertive, you would have complained. If you lacked confidence or self-esteem you may not have complained. You did not enjoy your meal. You would not go to that restaurant again. You did not feel valued as a customer or as a person. It almost goes without saying that you would have enjoyed your meal in a restaurant where the service was good and where the staff anticipated your needs. Burnard (1997) expresses the view that we care for others because we must. He puts it another way by saying that we are able to reflect on our own humanity and we are able to recognise the humanity of others. He presses the point by arguing that once we realise that the world is peopled with creatures like ourselves, we feel (or should feel) the need to treat those 'others' as we would want to be treated ourselves.

This is something that I identify strongly with. I felt pleased that I had given Margaret the opportunity to select her clothes. Our choice of clothing is an expression of how we feel about ourselves. Some days I want to look smart, others I just want to feel comfortable. But how I dress is an inherent part of me. Why should I presume to choose Margaret's clothes when she was capable of doing this for herself? There is little opportunity for choice in nursing home life. Meals are at the same time each day, and the daily routine tends to be structured around them. I therefore think that it is important to be flexible whenever possible. Little things can mean a lot. For example, I think Margaret was quite pleased to be asked whether or not she wanted a bubble bath.

Sometimes when I knock on residents' doors they will say, 'Oh, you do not need to do that'. But I think that I do. Their room is their home, their sanctuary, and their own personal space. I believe that this gesture conveys my respect for the person and their very limited privacy. Staff are often uncomfortable with having residents' room doors closed, they worry that the resident will perhaps fall or come to some other harm and not be seen. That is a valid argument, but I believe that we all have the right to be on our own, in our own space from time to time, and not be worried that someone is going to walk in without being invited.

Margaret's bell ringing was a cry for help. Yes, she was an attention seeker, but it was attention she deserved and needed. Peplau (1988) identified that all individuals have needs and that if these needs are not fulfilled, then tensions will arise and manifest themselves in a variety of ways. When these needs are fulfilled, then the individual will experience satisfaction. She proposed that:

All human behaviour is purposeful and goal seeking in terms of feelings of satisfaction and or/security.

When I entered Margaret's room for the second time that morning, I recognised her need. I touched her. Touch can have a multitude of meanings. Residents are physically handled many times each day. But in this context it was an instinctive gesture to communicate to Margaret that I wanted to listen to her. I had an interest in her and a commitment to help her. Minardi and Riley (1997) suggested that light touch, within an appropriate context, may stimulate catharsis, an expression of emotions. This form of communication may be particularly pertinent with clients such as Margaret who are visually impaired. She did respond positively to this touch. Other people, however, may feel threatened or compromised by touch. The nurse needs to be able to read cues carefully. Margaret did not attempt to withdraw; indeed, she visibly relaxed. I had to leave Margaret for a short time, which was regrettable but necessary. She appeared pleased to see me return. The moment was not lost.

I have already declared my own feelings of satisfaction following this interaction with Margaret. I believe that this is important. Jean Watson's *Philosophy and Science of Caring* (1989) explored a humanistic approach to nursing and the establishment of a trusting interpersonal relationship between nurse and client. She acknowledged that caring is an integral part of nursing, and that effective caring is satisfying for both nurse and client. However, this relationship requires acceptance of both positive and negative feelings and that something may be positive at an emotional level and negative at an intellectual level or vice versa.

On an emotional level I felt satisfaction that I had cared for Margaret, and that our interpersonal relationship would be ongoing. I talked to care assistants and discussed with them their feelings for Margaret. I explained her needs. I reinforced that the residents' privacy should be respected, and that they should be helped to maintain their dignity. If it is safe to do so, residents should be allowed to use the toilet in privacy. They should not be made to feel rushed. Comments should not be made about any odours produced. Generally, the untrained staff were committed to caring. Omissions were usually due to a gap in their training. They were motivated to learn. On an intellectual level though, I knew that nothing major had changed for Margaret. People did try, but she would continue to grieve for her lost husband, life and independence. She would continue to suffer the indignity of needing someone else to take her to the toilet. Her meals would be served at the times prescribed by nursing home routine and generally she would have little choice of what she ate. She would continue to have near-strangers walk into her room, sometimes unannounced. She would have people peer at her in the depths of the night to check that she was still breathing. Although she made use of the talking library, until her cataracts were removed she would not be able to read. She could not be persuaded to join in organised activities, or to eat in the dining room. It seemed likely that she would sit in Room 12, staring into the corridor, for the rest of her life.

'Empowerment' is a word frequently used in nursing theory and practice today (Ghaye *et al.*, 2000). It means different things to different people, but Rodwell's (1996) analysis of the literature concluded that empowerment involves facilitating a client's autonomy. By working to develop their self-esteem and a sense of value, they may be encouraged to take responsibility for their own health and decisions concerning their life. The nurse will need to accept that clients' decisions may have negative affects on their health. We had to provide Margaret with choices and options, but accept and respect her decisions.

I know that the care assistants cared about Margaret, as they cared about all the residents. Their work was very demanding and they were often very short staffed. Several had been working at this home for a number of years and were very dedicated. But when dependency levels and pressures of work are high, staff can become stressed. Bond (1986) suggested that at times like this, care staff might become irritable or lack the patience necessary to care effectively.

Rodwell's (1996) review of the literature indicated that for a health worker to be able to value her client sufficiently to facilitate empowerment, she needs to respect and value herself and her practice. On reflection, I think that is something to be aware of. Indeed, some of my analysis makes me feel uncomfortable. I sound judgmental and uncaring, and make excuses for myself. Perhaps at times I could have been more understanding, could have tried harder to relate to some of the residents. But I am a caring nurse. The well-being of my clients is the basis of my practice, and I communicate concerns about the organisation to the management team. Ongoing education of the care staff and increased management support at times of stress may improve their sense of worth. They need to know that they are valued and that they are doing a good job. Research by Sumaya-Smith (1995) indicated that close interpersonal relationships between care staff and residents was integral to staff retention. These 'surrogate family bonds' require considerable emotional investment by staff, but are greatly valued by staff and residents. I can identify with this. Although my relationship with Margaret has no history, it is ongoing. This is a privilege, and the reason I chose to work in a nursing home. My caring moment with Margaret was a clarifying moment. I enjoy working with elderly people, getting to know them and maybe making a real difference to their later years. I have been able to recognise that at times factors may threaten and hinder this.

Through reflecting on my practice in this chapter I feel that I am now in a much stronger position to provide, and to help others provide, the care that these people deserve.

References

Allen, J. (1996) A time and a place. *Nursing Standard*, **10**(17), 49.

Bond, M. (1986) *Stress And Self-Awareness: A Guide For Nurses*. Heinemann Nursing, Oxford.

Burnard, P. (1997) Why care? Ethical and spiritual issues in caring nursing. In: *Caring. The Compassion and Wisdom of Nursing* (ed. G. Brykczynska). Edward Arnold, London.

Ferry, R. (1994) Complex causes. *Nursing Times*, **90**(3), 34–5.

Ghaye, T., Gillespie, D. and Lillyman, S. (2000) *Empowerment through Reflection: The Narratives of Healthcare Professionals*. Quay Books, London.

Gibson, F. (1994) *Reminiscence And Recall: A Guide To Good Practice*. Age Concern England, London.

Harrison, A. (1998) A harmful procedure. *Nursing Times*, **94**(27), 37–8.

Millar, R. (1990) *Managing Difficult Patients*. Faber & Faber, London.

Minardi, H. A. and Riley, M. J. (1997) *Communication In Health Care: A Skills Based Approach*. Butterworth-Heinemann, Oxford.

Murray, I. (1998) At the cutting edge. *Nursing Times*, **94**(27), 37–7.

Patterson, B. J. (1995) The process of social support: adjusting to life in a nursing home. *Journal of Advanced Nursing*, **21**, 682–9.

Peplau, H. (1988) *Interpersonal Relations In Nursing*. Macmillan, London.

Rodwell, C. M. (1996) An analysis of the concept of empowerment. *Journal of Advanced Nursing*, **23**, 305–13.

Stockwell, F. (1972) *The Unpopular Patient*. Royal College of Nursing, London.

Sumaya-Smith, I. (1995) Caregiver/resident relationships: surrogate family bonds and surrogate grieving in a skilled nursing facility. *Journal of Advanced Nursing*, **21**, 447–51.

Watson, J. (1989) Philosophy and science of caring. In: *Nursing Theorists And Their Work* (ed. A. Marriner-Tomey). CV Mosby Company, St Louis.

CHAPTER 10

Caring moments with carers

Sue Lillyman

One group of people that are often forgotten are the unpaid carers, especially those caring for family and friends with long-term and life-limiting conditions. Potentially, any of us can become an unpaid carer for a family member or friend, and even though we might be healthcare professionals the role is different. In this chapter we will review the role of a carer and discuss a caring moment based on Ghaye *et al.*'s (2008) model of Positive Appreciative Reflection.

Who are the unpaid carers?

In the UK it is already estimated that each year over 301,000 adults become carers (Hirst, 1999) and an estimated 290,000 young people between the ages of 16–24 are already carers (Petch, 2009), with the age range for all carers from 5 years to people in their 90s (Barber, 2010). Most people are likely to become carers between the ages of 50 and 59 (Hughes, 2009). Currently, 1 in 8 adults in the UK are carers (Davies, 2010), which can often result in life-changing experience bringing rewards and challenges (Corry and While, 2009). This group of people who provide unpaid care save the NHS an estimated £6 billion a year (Barber, 2010) and are often taken for granted (Payne and Ellis-Hill, 2002).

As unpaid carers, these are people who may have been thrust into the role by circumstances (unlike professionals, who have chosen the caring profession), usually at short notice and without adequate preparation and information (Davies, 2010; Eyre, 2010; Glasper, 2009). The other major difference from the professional is that the unpaid carer is often a 24 hour, 7 days a week provider of care, whereas professionals can go home at the end of their shift. Barber (2010) notes it is not unusual for the carer to devote 40–50 hours a week or longer caring for family members.

There are often changes in the life circumstances of unpaid carers (Hasson *et al.*, 2010). Kelly (2010) also highlights changes in roles from son or daughter to carer for a parent, husband, wife or partner caring for their spouse, with carers losing their identity as wife, husband or partner. Other factors associated with this role include tension in those relationships and the strain of the role in relation to the psychological distress as the carer lives with the effects of the illness on their loved one (Kelly 2010). Lubkin (1986) also noted that the demands of taking on these new roles can result in emotional strain, guilt, resentment and frustration. On top of all this, unpaid carers often report suffering from depression, exhaustion, back problems, feelings of being trapped, fatigue, poor sleep patterns, anxiety, stress and sexual/relationship problems (Arber *et al.*, 2010; Aoun *et al.*, 2005; Borthwick *et al.*, 2009; Corry and While, 2008; Forbes *et al.*, 2007). In end of life care, Nolan (2001) noted that people took this role on for love, duty, desire to prevent institutional death and to carry out wishes. Gent *et al.* (2009) identified how some carers had said how they appreciated the time they had with their partners. However, Greenwood *et al.* (2008) and the Carers UK charity note that many carers are not given any choice in taking on this role.

Other positive rewards identified by carers included greater insight into illness and hardship of their loved one, interpersonal benefits such as companion gains, personal growth and becoming more patient, some strengthening of relationships, health gains for the cared for, and change in life priorities and personal goals (Corry and While, 2008).

The focus continues to remain on the cared for, rather than the carer. However, as noted above, the NHS has to rely on the carer.

Meeting the needs of the carer

The government has long recognised the needs of carers and their value in the provision of care through the following documents:

- Carers (Recognition and Services) Act 1995: set out to give legal status and entitlement for carers
- Carers and Disabled Children Act 2000: this provided direct payment for carers and entitled the provision of short breaks for the carer
- Carers (Equal Opportunities) Act 2004: identified the need for carer assessment, echoed by Glasper (2009)
- *National Service Framework for Long Term Conditions* (Department of Health, 2005)
- Work and Families Act 2006: provides flexible working arrangements for those caring for family members
- *High Quality Care for All: NHS Next Stage Review Final Report* (Darzi Report) (Lord Darzi, 2008): recognised the crucial role that is played by the unpaid carer

- Children and Young Persons Act 2008
- *Carers at the Heart of 21st Century Families and Communities* (Department of Health, 2008): stated that the needs and aspirations of the carer should be recognised and that they should be free to have separate identity and make the position of unpaid carer more transparent within society.
- *Shaping the Future of Care Together* (Department of Health, 2009)
- *National Service Framework for Older People* (Department of Health, 2006)
- World Health Organization's Palliative Care
- *Commissioning for Carers* (2009): should deliver outcomes for carers as well as those in receipt of care

However, with all these documents and policies in place there is still a wealth of research-based evidence to identify how the carers' needs are not being recognised and met within the UK.

The main issues faced by carers can be themed as follows:

- Limited, or no, training in relation to physical, psychosocial and emotional care for the role (Arber *et al.*, 2010; Eyre, 2010; Borthwick *et al.*, 2009); as Davies (2010) points out, the carer often learns through trial and error
- Provision of, and access to, information in relation to the condition of the person they are caring for (Arber *et al.*, 2010; Gold *et al.*, 2009; Salin *et al.*, 2009; Whittingham, 2009). Glasper (2009) noted that this was the key to empowering carers in their role
- Recognition of ethnicity and cultural values and the diversity within ethnic groups (Strudwick and Morris, 2010)
- Provision of resources such as respite care (Stirling *et al.*, 2010)
- Support from professionals and peers (Arber *et al.*, 2010; Hasson *et al.*, 2010; Salin *et al.*, 2009); as Thomas *et al.* (2010) note, this is usually crisis-driven when it is given
- Being recognised by practitioners (Greenwood *et al.*, 2010)
- Becoming part of the care team (Salin *et al.*, 2009)
- Choice and autonomy (Greenwood *et al.*, 2010)
- Timely and responsive services to prevent crisis management (Gent *et al.*, 2009)
- Insufficient rest and reduced personal time (Briggs, 2010; Cochrane *et al.*, 1997)
- Making assumptions about carers' ability or willingness to care (Department of Health, 1999)
- Disempowerment on admission to hospital (Princess Royal Trust, 2003)

The carer as a partner in care

If we are to recognise carers and rely on them within their role as carers, then they should be involved at every level. They should be placed at the centre of care with the one being cared for, but with a recognition that their needs might be different from the person being cared for (Borthwick *et al.*, 2009). Glasper (2009) reminds us that as professionals we must not forget that our caring activities are only a small part of the overall provision of care administered by these unpaid carers, and nurses need to value family members as partners in care and as part of the multiprofessional team. Gent *et al.* (2009) go on to identify that this is a mutual journey of discovery for the carer and the professional, and through this we all can learn and develop skills and knowledge. As Salin (2009) also points out, we share common goals. The *Commissioning for Carers* (2009) document noted that carers should be treated as experts and care partners, and Greenwood *et al.*, (2010) endorsed this by saying that they should be offered increased control over care provision. However, this can lead to a conflict with the professional's personal, ethical and aesthetic knowledge, as identified by Carper (1978), and this is discussed later in this chapter.

Discourse in relation to information giving

If the nurse or professional recognises the carer as an equal partner and expert in care, as suggested by Greenwood *et al.* (2010), Salin *et al.* (2009), Glasper (2009) and the Department of Health (2008, 2009a,b) then this should be embraced at all levels. One such area that has been highlighted and which might cause conflict for the professional is in the area of confidentiality. As professionals we are to abide by our codes of conduct (i.e. Nursing and Midwifery Council, 2008). The need for information about the care and condition required by the carer to provide the care needed is problematic. As Morris and Thomas (2002) point out, the carer and cared for often see themselves as one unit and therefore the professional should give equal weighting to both. Gold *et al.* (2009) notes that the conflict between the person being cared for's right to privacy and the carer's expectation means that the professional is caught up in the western philosophical tradition, which provides the professional with a climate of ethical and legislative limitations. On the one hand we are recognise the carer, and on the other we maintain patient confidentiality. The White Paper *Liberating the NHS* (Department of Health, 2010) echoes this in the statement 'nothing done to me without me'. Although we do not advocate that patients are not involved in decision making, there is a place to recognise the carer in that decision making process.

Working through a caring moment, caring for the carer

In all my professional life I have never heard anyone state that unpaid carers are not valued and needed in order to participate in the patient's care. They are vital to the wellbeing of the one being cared for, and as a healthcare service we could not cope without people to care for their loved ones and friends within society. These are our espoused values as a society and as professionals. However, in practice our values in action, by nature of our own governing guidelines, show that we do the opposite. Carers are not often seen or valued as an expert and multiprofessional member of the team. We struggle with giving them information on which they can base the care they are providing due to the ethical and legislative constraints of the codes of conduct we work to set down by government, our professional bodies and employers. In the following caring moment we review how, when facing this type of ethical issue, we can act in a manner that is congruent with our espoused caring values.

Contextual grounding

A nurse had been asked by the general practitioner to visit an elderly couple, Mary and Bob, in their home to assess them for health and social care needs. Bob was suffering from cancer of the prostate which had now spread to most of his internal organs. He was on morphine and his prognosis was poor. Bob was nevertheless the main carer for his wife Mary, who was almost immobile having had a stroke five years previously which had left her blind in one eye and paralysed down the left side of her body.

After ringing the doorbell the nurse waited about ten minutes whilst Bob made his way to the door. She could hear him shouting for me to wait as he struggled to walk to the door. Bob appeared slow and had limited mobility. He was 82 years of age. As he guided her back to the sitting room he held on to pieces of furniture to support himself. The house appeared clean but cluttered, and she noticed that a stair lift had been fitted. The initial assessment was that he required a referral to an occupational therapist for more resources in the home to assist him with his mobility. As a nurse, the 'fixing it' mentality was at work. What a nurse would need to do to make things work was foremost in her mind, rather then finding out what the couple actually needed.

On entering the room she was greeted by Mary, also 82 years old, who was sitting in an armchair, unable to get up. There was a Zimmer frame by her chair and a table with drinks and sweets within reach. Bob explained who the nurse was and that she had come to see her. He was Mary's carer and Mary was the one being cared for. Bob had been looking after Mary for the last 15 years since her first stroke, which had left her with limited mobility and loss of sight in one eye.

The nurse looked around the cluttered room. Although clean, it was in desperate need of a tidy-up, and the scatter rugs on the floor screamed out to her to be moved, as this was potentially a danger in relation to falls. The nurse started to talk to Mary, but her hearing aid was not working and she had poor eyesight so communication was difficult. Bob went to the kitchen to make a pot of tea. The nurse asked Mary if it was OK to talk in front of Bob about her condition and needs, and she willingly gave her consent. Bob returned and started to talk for Mary and tell the nurse about how he cared for his wife. Both were happy in this situation and comfortable with each other. There was no conflict for the nurse in talking openly with either of them.

Bob told the nurse how their son and daughter-in-law visited once a week, did some housework and bought some food that was stored in the freezer for him to use during the week. He maintained the house the rest of the week and kept on top of the gardening, although he had recently suffered a fall whilst trying to climb steps to clean the outside windows. He showed the nurse a large graze on his arm and swollen leg for which he had not had any medical attention. She noticed straight way that the cut was infected and the leg red and swollen.

They talked about Mary's general health and care. Bob was adamant that he did not want any help from outside; he did not want strangers in his house. It was obvious to the nurse as a professional that Bob's health was starting to deteriorate and that the situation could not continue for much longer. They were willing to have the nurse visit and for the GP to provide a medical check-up but no more. Their second son, who had been divorced, now lived in the house with Bob and Mary, but was at work at the time of the nurse's visit. The nurse then discussed their son's input into their care. Bob and Mary did not want to 'burden him' with their health issues, as he was their son and he 'needed a life of his own'. He had gone through a lot with his divorce and needed to settle down again. They did not want him involved in any discussion about their health as he should not feel under any obligation to look after them in their old age. Bob and Mary said they could cope on their own without help.

On returning to the surgery the nurse had a visit from Bob and Mary's son. He explained that he was now the main carer for both parents and was involved in their care. He actually did most of the caring work, and although his father did try to cook and keep on top of the gardening, this was now starting to affect his father's health. He could see there was a major problem and was asking me for support and information about how to care for his parents. He wanted to know how both his parents' health would progress over time. He was not aware of his father's diagnosis, although he could see he was not a well man. He asked what his father's condition was and what could be done to help him get some strength back. Did he need to give up work and what were the options available to him to help him care for his parents? The son also reported that he was feeling depressed due to the situation at home, as neither parent acknowledged his input into their care. He was exhausted from work and coming home to care for the two of them, and physically he was beginning to feel 'worn out'. He stated that 'at 58 years of age I am no spring chicken either and do not know how much longer I can cope with the two of them'. He was aware that neither wanted to go into residential care and he also wanted them to remain together for as long as possible. He explained that his mother was now incontinent and that he was getting up three or four times a night to help her on to the commode. He helped his father take care of her personal care and kept on top of the housework. Both parents had poor appetites and he was too exhausted to eat when he came home from his part-time job at the local supermarket. The son looked worn out and pale, but said his job was his saving grace as he needed to 'escape from the house'.

Conscious work habits

Ghaye *et al.* (2008) note that the conscious values are the values that guide what we do. As a professional the issue of confidentiality was uppermost in the nurses mind. As professionals we are bound by our professional guidelines, such as the code of conduct (Nursing and Midwifery Council, 2008), the General Medical Council's *Good Medical Practice* (2006) and *Confidentiality* (2009), and the Health Professions Council's *Standards of Conduct Performance & Ethics* (2008); the Human Rights Act 1998; the Data Protection Act 1998; employers' policies and organisational standards; and common law; all of which require the professional to maintain the confidentiality of the person in their care.

Both parents had capacity and told the nurse that they did not want their son 'concerned' or 'burdened' with their health concerns. They also did not want 'outside help' and did not see the stress that this situation was causing their son and how his mental and physical wellbeing was being affected by the situation. To talk with the son would be a direct breach of confidentiality, as set out in Nursing and Midwifery Council (2008, p. 8): 'you must respect people's right to confidentially'. However, another part of the code states (p. 3) 'work with others to protect and promote health and wellbeing of those in your care, their families, carers and wider community'. At that point in time the nurse only listened to the son and provided some comfort as he shared his concerns.

Supported work habit

Here we identify feelings. In this situation the nurse felt frustrated, as her personal and professional values were in conflict with each other: wanted to maintain confidentially for the patient and her husband, but also wanted to help the son care for his parents. There were also two professional values in conflict: on the one hand she had to maintain the confidentiality of her patient, while on the other she had a duty to the son and his wellbeing.

Mental work habit

Working through the issues raised above in relation to the carer as a member of the multidisciplinary team and the needs of the son in the future care of his parents, there was a need to identify the conflicting values and address them in relation to the professional code and best interest of the patients. The wife and her husband wanted to remain as independent as possible and not rely on the son; however, they were actually causing more concern by not letting him help and having open discussions.

Practical work habits

Ghaye *et al.* (2008) refer to building services and the strengths of a team approach. They refer to what is called 'collective wisdom'. Gaining support from colleagues is not weakness but a strength of any team. Through discussion and conversations, such as through clinical supervision (Lillyman and Ghaye, 2010) or in team meetings, we can support each other and help gain a wider picture of the issue at hand. Here the issue was shared with other members of the multidisciplinary team and there was a full conversation about the ethical and professional issues involved in relation to the breach of any confidential issues. The culture (what Ghaye *et al.* (2008) refer to as the political working habit) was supportive and fostered those critical conversations amongst professionals. In this situation it was felt that a joint visit should be undertaken by the nurse and GP to discuss the situation with the parents, without the son present, but to identify their needs and expected outcomes of their conditions should they refuse help from their son. In doing this the situation was able to move forward and both accepted that they needed their son more. A further conversation was undertaken with the couple and their son and an agreement was made and goals set in relation to achieve the most independence possible.

Conclusion

In this situation it may seem easy to react to instincts such as breaching confidentiality 'in the best interest'. However, on reflection trust can be lost or even professional standing bought into question if this is done without reviewing the options. Gaining that collective wisdom and working as a team, especially in this type of situation, can help to value carers, keep the patient at the centre and ensure that the best possible care is provided without a conflict in values.

References

Aoun, S. M., Kristjanson, L. J., Currow, D. C. and Hudson, P. L. (2005) Caregiving for the terminally ill: at what cost? *Palliative Medicine*, **19**(7), 551–5.

Arber, A., Hutson, N., Guerrero, D., Wilson, S., Lucas, C. and Faithful, S. (2010) Carers of patients with primary malignant brain tumour: are their information needs met? *British Journal of Neuroscience Nursing*, **6**(7), 329–34.

Barber, C. (2010) Celebrate carers all year round. *British Journal of Healthcare Assistants*, **4**(7), 358.

Borthwick, R., Newbronner, L. and Stuttard, L. (2009) 'Out of hospital': a scoping study of services for carers of people being discharged from hospital. *Health and Social Care in the Community*, **17**(4), 335–49.

Briggs, D. (2010) Notes on end of life: the social interactions between patient, carer and professional. *Quality in Ageing and Older Adults*, **11**(2), 35–46.

Carper, B. (1978) Fundamental patterns of knowing. *Advances in Nursing Science*, **1**, 13–23.

Cochrane, J. J., Goering, P. N. and Rogers, J. M. (1997) The mental health of informal caregivers in Ontario: an epidemiological survey. *American Journal of Public Health*, **87**(12), 2002–7.

Corry, M. and While, A. (2009) The needs of carers of people with multiple sclerosis a literature review. *Scandinavian Journal of Caring Science*, **23**, 569–588.

Davies, C. (2010). A training course that empowers hard-to-reach carers. *Nursing Older People*, **22**(10), 28–30.

Department of Health (1999) *Caring About Carers: A National Strategy for Carers*. Department of Health, London.

Department of Health (2005) *National Service Framework for Long Term Conditions*. Department of Health, London.

Department of Health (2006) *National Service Framework for Older People*. Department of Health, London.

Department of Health (2008) *Carers at the Heart of 21st Century Families and Communities*. Department of Health, London.

Department of Health (2009a) *Shaping the Future of Care Together*. Department of Health, London.

Department of Health (2009b) *Commissioning for Carers*. Department of Health, London.

Department of Health (2010) *Liberating the NHS*. Department of Health, London.

Eyre, S. (2010) Supporting informal carers of dying patients: the District Nurse's role. *Nursing Standard*, **24**(22), 43–8.

Forbes, A., While, A. and Mathes, L. (2007) Informal carer activities, care burden and health status in multiple sclerosis. *Clinical Rehabilitation*, **21**, 563–75.

General Medical Council (2006) *Good Medical Practice*. GMC, London.

General Medical Council (2009) *Confidentiality*. GMC, London.

Gent, C., McGarry, J. and Pinnington, L. (2009) Motor neurone disease: cares' experiences behaviour and coping methods. *British Journal of Neuroscience Nursing*, **5**(12), 567–73.

Ghaye, T., Melander-Wikman, A., Kaisare, M., Chambers, P., Bergmark, U., Kostenius, C, and Lillyman, S. (2008) Participatory and appreciative action and reflection (PAAR) – democratizing reflective practices. *Reflective Practice*, **9**(4), 361–98.

Glasper, A. (2009) An appraisal of the first annual report of the standing commission on carers. *British Journal of Nursing*, **18**(22), 1416–17.

Gold, M., Philip, J., Melver, S. and Komesaroff, P. A. (2009) Between a rock and a hard place: exploring the conflict between respecting privacy of patients and informing their carers. *Internal Medicine Journal*, **39**, 582–7.

Greenwood, N., MacKenzie, A., Cloud, G. C. and Wilson, N. (2008) Informal carers of stroke survivors – factors influencing carers: a systematic review of quantitative studies. *Disability and Rehabilitation*, **30**(18), 1329–49.

Greenwood, N., MacKenzie, A., Cloud, G. C. and Wilson, N. (2010) Loss of autonomy, control and independence when caring: a qualitative study of informal carers of stroke survivors in the first three months after discharge. *Disability and Rehabilitation*, **32**(2), 125–133.

Health Professions Council (2008) *Standards of Conduct, Performance and Ethics*. HPC, London.

Hasson, F., Kernohan, W. G., McLaughlin, M., Waldron, M., McLaughlin, D., Chambers, H. and Cochrane, B. (2010) An exploration into the palliative and end-of-life experiences of carers of people with Parkinson's disease. *Palliative Medicine*, **24**(7), 731–6.

Hughes, R. (2009) Support for carers. *British Journal of Healthcare Assistants*, **3**(11), 566.

Hirst, M. (1999) *The Risk of Informal Care: an Incidence Study*. Social Policy Research Unit, University of York.

Kelly, M. (2010) Who cares... for the carer? *Journal of Renal Care*, **36**(1), 16–20.

Lillyman, S. and Ghaye, T. (2010) *Effective Clinical Supervision. The Role of Reflection*. Quay Books, London.

Lord Darzi (2008) *High Quality Care for All: Nhs Next Stage Review Full Report*. Stationery Office, London.

Lubkin, I. M. (1986) *Chronic Illness – Impact and Interventions*. Jones and Bartlett Publishers, Boston/Monterey.

Morris, S. and Thomas, C. (2002) The need to know; informal carers and information. *European Journal of Cancer*, **11**, 183–7.

Nolan, M. R. (2001) Positive aspects of caring. In: *Chronic and Terminal Illness: New Perspectives on Caring and Carers* (eds. S. Payne and C. Ellis-Hill), pp. 22–43. Oxford University Press, Oxford.

Nursing and Midwifery Council (2008) *The Code: Standards of Conduct, Performance and Ethics for Nurses and Midwives*. NMC, London.

Payne, S. and Ellis-Hill, C. (eds.) (2002) *Chronic and Terminal Illness: New Perspectives on Caring and Carers*. Oxford University Press, Oxford.

Petch, A. (2009) The experiences and needs of young adult carers in the UK. Community Care, **13**(3), 30–1.

Princess Royal Trust (2003) *Focus on Carers and the NHS – Identifying and Supporting Hidden Carers*. PRTC, Glasgow.

Salin, S., Kaunones, M. and Astedt-Kurki, P. (2009) Informal carers of older family members: how they manage and what support they receive from respite care. *Journal of Clinical Nursing*, **18**, 492–501.

Stirling, C., Andrews, S., Croft, T., Vickers, J., Turner, P. and Robinson, A. (2010) Measuring dementia carers' unmet need for services – an exploratory mixed method study. *BMC Health Services Research*, **10**, 122.

Strudwick, A. and Morris, R. (2010). A qualitative study exploring the experiences of African-Caribbean informal stroke carers in the UK. *Clinical Rehabilitation*, **24**, 159–67.

Thomas, K., Hudson, P., Oldham, L., Kelly, A. and Trauer, T. (2010) Meeting the needs of family carers: an evaluation of three home-based palliative acre services in Australia. *Palliative Medicine*, **24**(2), 183–91.

Whittingham, K. (2009) The physical and psychological impact of being an unpaid carer for heart failure patients. *British Journal of Cardiac Nursing*, **4**(8), 354–8.

CHAPTER 11

Dehumanising caring moments?

Jo Hamilton-Jones

What follows stands in sharp contrast to the qualitative accounts of practice presented earlier. In this chapter, I am going to illustrate how information technology (IT) can be used to enhance reflection. The main goal is to show how IT can help us to understand certain clinical situations more clearly, deeply and richly – in other words, to make more sense of them so that we can perhaps act more effectively, confidently and safely. In order to gain the most from this chapter, we first need to become familiar with the key ideas of modelling and simulation. Brace yourself. The language used is different from the first person reflections in earlier chapters. It will challenge you. It is a different way of seeing and understanding.

The process of modelling and simulation lies at the centre of many methods of computer analysis (Rothery, 1990, pp. 1–6, 47–60). The idea of modelling can be understood, for example, with regard to a flight simulator. The simulation is made to be as realistic as possible in order to understand the nature of flying and the complex decisions that need to be made in a context of lots of things happening at once and unpredictably. The simulation can also help us to reflect-in-action, think on our feet and resolve problems and difficulties as they arise. It is not only the flying operation which is modelled. The effect of the weather on the plane is being modelled too. This system includes many of the features of reality that influence the progress and outcome of the situation.

We can use modelling in an investigative way in healthcare, particularly when the user is trying to understand something better in order to make more rational, planned and principled decisions. One kind of modelling, called spreadsheet modelling, can help us develop our skilfulness in the decision-making process. Among other functions, the computer can be used to carry out some mathematical computations. Using a spreadsheet enables complicated analyses to be undertaken without getting into time-consuming and complicated calculations.

This chapter illustrates one of the many uses of information technology. It simulates some real-life situations which will be familiar to a number of healthcare professionals. The first simulation is called 'the doctor's waiting room'. In order to achieve the aims stated above I have tried to help us see it differently and to think again about it by applying a well-known mathematical queueing problem. I then go on to develop the idea of modelling and simulation and how it can help us in our healthcare work by drawing on more complex situations which, for example, could occur in a hospital department. This chapter is not intended to be a completely definitive solution to such problems. Rather the intention is to show how IT can be used to help us to reflect on practice, encourage ideas and inspire confidence to be creative in the resolution of everyday problems. In this sense IT is an invaluable aid to reflective practices.

Doctor's waiting room – no appointments

In 1962, the Operational Research Society and the Ministry of Health arranged a discussion on the subject of appointment systems in hospitals and general practice. One of the papers dealt with the design of an appointment system for a GP's morning surgery, which ran theoretically from 9:00 a.m. to 11:00 a.m. Before the appointment system, patients began to arrive at about 8:00 a.m. and a queue of up to 10 people had usually formed by the time the surgery doors were opened at 8.30 a.m. By 9:00 a.m. the queue had increased to up to 30 people, overflowing the waiting room. This, together with the fact that the doctor was often late, meant that patients had to wait a very long time – about an hour and a half on average.

The paper considered a GP working on his own. In 'queueing language', this is a single service station with a 'first come, first served' queue discipline (Figure 11.1).

Although this model could be considered to be relatively 'simple' in today's real-life scenarios, it provides a suitable starting position for the analysis.

To continue the analysis, in order to specify such a system, we need to know:

■ the distribution (pattern) of the doctor's consulting time
■ the nature of the arrival pattern of the patients

Figure 11.1 A doctor's waiting room model.

Table 11.1 Results from data collection in 1962.

Length of consultation time in minutes	Average length of consultation time in minutes	Percentage of patients with each consulting time
0.5–1.499	1	10
1.5–2.499	2	16
2.5–3.499	3	18
3.5–4.499	4	16
4.5–5.499	5	12
5.5–6.499	6	10
6.5–7.499	7	6
7.5–8.499	8	4
8.5–9.499	9	3
9.5–10.499	10	2
10.5–11.499	11	0
11.5–12.499	12	0
12.5–13.499	13	0
13.5–14.499	14	0
14.5–15.499	15	0
15.5–16.499	16	1
16.5–17.499	17	0
17.5–18.499	18	0
18.5–19.499	19	2
19.5–20.499	20	0

From the 800 observations collected in 1962, the work was developed further (Lighthill, 1978, pp. 249–59) and Table 11.1 and Figure 11.2 show the resulting percentage frequency distribution.

For ease of calculation, some approximations have been made; any consulting times occurring between 2.5 min and 3.499 min were allocated the consulting time of 3 min. From Table 11.1 and Figure 11.2, we can see that the majority of the consultations lasted less than 10 minutes with the average consulting time of 4.55 minutes per patient. Table 11.1 also highlights the percentage of patients associated with each consultation length. In statistical terms, this could be

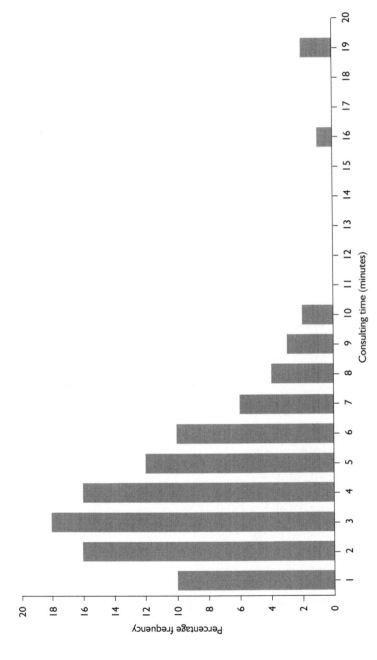

Figure 11.2 Bar chart of doctor's consulting time.

described as the 'percentage frequency'. These results provide the structure or 'frequency distribution' on which to base the simulation.

Doctor's waiting room – appointment system

Consider the situation if an appointment system was implemented. Patients would arrive at prescribed and preferably regular intervals. The object of the exercise would be to determine the best value of the interval between appointments. However, secondary factors are also of interest, e.g. the time that patients spend waiting to see the doctor and the time doctors spend waiting for patients to arrive (i.e. the time between one patient leaving and the next patient arriving).

Let us say that we want to reflect on the effect of changing the patient inter-arrival interval and the effect this has on the average time that patients spend waiting to see the doctor and the total time that the doctor spends waiting to start a consultation. If this is our intention the next task is to generate a simulation that will enable us to compare the results for different appointment times. In order to make the simulation as lifelike as possible, we need to build the simulated pattern of consultation times around original, empirical (real-world) data. In this case, we shall use the data from Table 11.1. However, real-life data can be collected more fitting to a particular situation and adapted accordingly.

Appointments are often scheduled for regular time intervals. We need to be able to experiment to determine which time interval would provide the best possible service for the patient and the doctor. As an initial attempt, let us consider the situation where appointments are scheduled every four minutes, i.e. for a surgery starting at 9:00 a.m. the appointments would be made for 9:00 a.m., 9:04 a.m., 9:08 a.m., 9:12 a.m. and so on. In 'queueing' terminology, we call this an 'inter-arrival time' of four minutes.

Now we want to simulate the length of the consultation process. We have assumed here that each patient arrives at the surgery at the scheduled time of their appointment. In real life, of course, we know that this is not always the case. However, this assumption was made at this stage in order to keep the analysis as straightforward as possible. The start of each consultation will be affected by the finishing time of the previous consultation. If the patient arrives at the surgery, given the assumptions above, and the doctor is free, then the consultation can start immediately. However, if the patient arrives and previous consultation(s) are still under way, then the patient has to wait.

From the earlier data collection, we know that there is a pattern in the length of consulting times. The aim here is to generate a similar pattern and thereby produce a simulation that behaves in a very similar manner. We do this by generating a series of random numbers and then 'fit' these into the distribution or pattern developed before.

Some basic spreadsheet information

At this stage, we need to start using a spreadsheet to 'build' the simulation model. It is worth devoting some time here to provide a brief explanation of spreadsheet terms. Spreadsheet software creates a worksheet consisting of rows and columns (Figure 11.3). The rows are numbered 1, 2, 3,... and the columns are identified by letters, A, B, C,... with double letters (AA, AB,...) used beyond the 26th column. The intersection of a row and column is called a cell. A cell is identified by a cell reference or cell address, which consists of the column letter followed by the row number.

A user can enter three types of information into a cell in a worksheet. One is a number, another is text and another is a formula. In a formula, the user refers to other cells to identify the data in the computation and mathematical symbols to specify what type of computation is to be performed.

In this work, I have used Microsoft Excel on a personal computer. There are a considerable number of pre-programmed formulae within this version of Excel. I have used certain functions, for example LOOKUP, RAND(), SUM, IF, MAX and LARGE. Further explanations of these terms are included in the following text. In addition, there are special Help facilities within the package. Although the text of this chapter refers to the use of Excel, the simulations which follow could be built on other types of computers with alternative spreadsheet packages.

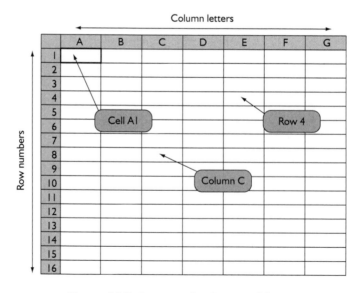

Figure 11.3 An example of a spreadsheet.

Using a spreadsheet to build the model

Table 11.2 is formed from the last two columns of Table 11.1. This forms the distribution or pattern for the simulation to be built on. This table could be contained in a separate worksheet or could be placed within the operating worksheet. The frequencies from Table 11.1 are added together one by one to form a 'cumulative' percentage frequency. Associated with each of these results is an average length of each consultation. Random numbers can be generated using several functions. The RAND() function within Excel will generate random numbers between 0 and 1, e.g. 0.6, 0.54. In order to 'fit' these into a specific pattern, we use the LOOKUP function. An example of this is given in Table 11.2.

Table 11.2 LOOKUP table for the doctor's waiting room.

	A	B	C
1	Cumulative percentage	Average consultation	Random number
2	of patients with each	length	
3	consulting time		
4	0	1	58
5	10	2	
6	26	3	
7	44	4	
8	60	5	
9	72	6	
10	82	7	
11	88	8	
12	92	9	
13	95	10	
14	97	16	
15	98	19	

Using the command:

LOOKUP (C4, A4:A15, B4:B15)

Location of random number   Location of cumulative percentage frequencies   Location of consultation lengths we can search through the data in Table 11.2 and build up an appropriate 'pattern' of values. As the frequencies are percentages, they lie between 0 and 100 and they will have a total of 100. Consequently, the random numbers need to be generated over the same range. This can be achieved by multiplying each random number by 100.

For example, suppose the random number is 58 in cell C4. The command LOOKUP(C4, A4:A15, B4:B15) would consider the value of C4, which is 58. It would compare it with the values in cells A4, A5, A6, ..., A15 and determine the percentage frequency values which immediately surround the value. In this case, these would be 44 and 60. Each of these values have TIME values associated with them from column B, i.e. 4 and 5. The lower of these is taken and the returned value for TIME would be 4.

Table 11.3 shows a simulated sequence of events for a two-hour surgery where patients can make appointments at specified four-minute intervals. To provide an insight into the workings of this simulation, let us proceed through the simulation in a step-by-step manner.

- *Appointment time* (column B) represents the time of each appointment. In equation form, this is calculated by adding four to the previous appointment time, e.g.

  time of appointment = time of previous appointment + 4

- *Start time of each consultation* (column C) represents the time that each patient starts their consultation. Towards the beginning of surgery, this is very similar to arrival time. However later in the simulation, as the queue builds up, the value is given by the finishing time of the previous consultation. This is formed using the IF statement in Excel.

- *Consultation start time*: if the previous consultation finishes later than the appointment time, then this consultation starts when the previous consultation finishes. Otherwise, this consultation starts at the scheduled appointment time.

For example, from Table 11.3 we have:

Cell C8 = IF (F7>B8, F7, B8)

| New consulting time | Does previous consultation finish after this appointment time? | If yes, then this consultation starts when the previous one ends | If no, then this consultation starts at the appointment time |

Table 11.3 Simulation of a doctor's waiting room with appointments every four minutes.

	A	B	C	D	E	F	G	H
1			Inter-appointment time				4 min	
2								
3								
4	Patient number	Scheduled appoint-ment time (min)	Start time of each consulta-tion (min)	Random number	Length of consulta-tion (min)	Finish time of each con-sultation (min)	Doctor's waiting time (min)	Patient waiting time (min)
5	1	0	0	66	5	5	0	0
6	2	4	5	85	7	12	0	1
7	3	8	12	10	2	14	0	4
8	4	12	14	26	3	17	0	2
9	5	16	17	7	1	18	0	1
10	6	20	20	6	1	21	2	0
11	7	24	24	53	4	28	3	0
12	8	28	28	28	3	31	0	0
13	9	32	32	49	4	36	1	0
14	10	36	36	89	8	44	0	0
15	11	40	44	1	1	45	0	4
16	12	44	45	85	7	52	0	1
17	13	48	52	36	3	55	0	4
18	14	52	55	85	7	62	0	3
19	15	56	62	33	3	65	0	6
20	16	60	65	57	4	69	0	5
21	17	64	69	25	2	71	0	5
22	18	68	71	6	1	72	0	3
23	19	72	72	82	7	79	0	0
24	20	76	79	65	5	84	0	3
25	21	80	84	56	4	88	0	4
26	22	84	88	23	2	90	0	4
27	23	88	90	62	5	95	0	2
28	24	92	95	88	8	103	0	3
29	25	96	103	11	2	105	0	7
30	26	100	105	94	9	114	0	5
31	27	104	114	98	19	133	0	10
32	28	108	133	96	10	143	0	25
33	29	112	143	19	2	145	0	31
34	30	116	145	39	3	148	0	29
35	31	120	148	93	9	157	0	28
	Average total				4.87096774		6	6.129032

117

- *Random number* (column D) consists of a sequence of two-digit random numbers, each multiplied by 100, as previously explained.
- *Length of consultation* (column E) represents the time that each consultation lasts. The first random number generated is 66. Using the LOOKUP feature of EXCEL as detailed earlier, this falls within the range of 60–72 of Table 11.2, and so the consulting time for the first patient is taken as 5 minutes. The next random number generated is 85. This falls in the range 82–88 of Table 11.2. The consulting time for the second patient is therefore taken as seven minutes.
- *Doctor's waiting time* (column G) represents the length of time that the doctor is kept waiting for each patient to arrive for each consultation. If the finishing time of the previous consultation is less than the start of the next appointment, then the doctor will be kept waiting. This is generated If the previous consultation finishes before the scheduled time of the next appointment.

For example, for cell G10, cell F9 is compared with cell B10. As the value of F9 (18) is less than B10 (20), this indicates that the doctor had to wait for the next patient. In spreadsheet terms, using Table 11.3, this is written as

IF (F9>B10, B10–F9, 0)

Does previous con-	If yes, calculate the	If no, then
sultation finish before	waiting time,	generate a
the next appointment	i.e. B10–F9	zero result
time?		

- *Patient's waiting time* (column H) represents the length of time that each patient is kept waiting to see the doctor. If the finishing time of the previous consultation is greater than the start of the next appointment, then the patient will be kept waiting.

For example, in Table 11.3, for cell H7, cell B7 is compared to C7. As the value of B7, the scheduled appointment time (8 min), is less than C7, the start of the consultation (12 min), then the patient has to wait.

In spreadsheet terms, using Table 11.3, this is generated from

Cell H7 = IF (B7>C7, C7–B7, 0)

Patient waiting	Does the next con-	If yes, calculate	If no, generate
time	sultation begin after	the waiting time,	a zero result
	this scheduled	i.e. C7–B7	
	appointment time?		

Table 11.4 Simulation of a doctor's waiting room with appointments every five minutes.

	A	B	C	D	E	F	G	H
1			Inter-appointment time				5 min	
2								
3								
4	Patient number	Scheduled appointment time (min)	Start time of each consultation (min)	Random number	Length of consultation (min)	Finish time of each consultation (min)	Doctor's waiting time (min)	Patient waiting time (min)
5	1	0	0	55	4	4	0	0
6	2	5	5	49	4	9	1	0
7	3	10	10	2	1	11	1	0
8	4	15	15	17	2	17	4	0
9	5	20	20	92	9	29	3	0
10	6	25	29	20	2	31	0	4
11	7	30	31	55	4	35	0	1
12	8	35	35	7	1	36	0	0
13	9	40	40	37	3	43	4	0
14	10	45	45	32	3	48	2	0
15	11	50	50	91	8	58	2	0
16	12	55	58	23	2	60	0	3
17	13	60	60	50	4	64	0	0
18	14	65	65	52	4	69	1	0
19	15	70	70	15	2	72	1	0
20	16	75	75	43	3	78	3	0
21	17	80	80	37	3	83	2	0
22	18	85	85	83	7	92	2	0
23	19	90	92	72	6	98	0	2
24	20	95	98	38	3	101	0	3
25	21	100	101	52	4	105	0	1
26	22	105	105	68	5	110	0	0
27	23	110	110	30	3	113	0	0
28	24	115	115	42	3	118	2	0
29	25	120	120	15	2	122	2	0
	Average total				3.68		30.00	0.56

The simulation continues for the two-hour period. At the end, it is possible to calculate the average waiting time for the doctor and also for the patient using the AVERAGE function within Excel.

One of the main purposes of this simulation is to enable experimentation with several intervals between appointments. For an inter-arrival time of five minutes, Table 11.4 provides the simulation results over a similar two-hour period.

Table 11.5 Comparison of appointment times.

	Average consulting time	Average patient wait time	Total doctor wait time
4 min	4.87	6.13	6
5 min	3.68	0.56	30
6 min	4.55	0.95	28
7 min	3.78	0.11	55
8 min	4.75	0.06	53
9 min	3.79	0.00	67
10 min	5.77	0.92	50

Running the simulation using several appointment intervals provides the information generated in Table 11.5.

Each run of the simulation uses a different set of random numbers. A different set of random numbers produces a different prediction. One spreadsheet is not enough. To see the consequences of the model, the simulation needs to be run several times, each with a different set of random numbers. This way, it will become apparent how long the patients' and doctor's waiting time will vary over time.

This form of simulation would assist in deciding appropriate appointment intervals for a typical doctor's practice where there is one doctor, i.e. one service outlet. However, we need to develop the model to try to make it more life-like and therefore more useful.

A hospital scenario – model I

Consider the situation where patients arrive at a hospital for emergency treatment (Figure 11.4). In this scenario, patients do not have 'fixed' appointment times, i.e. they arrive at unspecified intervals. I have used an arrival rate of 5 (i.e. on average, one patient arrives every five minutes) and a completion rate of 3 (i.e. on average, one patient takes three minutes) to complete their treatment (Table 11.6).

Patient arrives and joins the queue → Consultation with doctor → Patient leaves

Figure 11.4 Hospital model with one doctor.

Table 11.6 Simulation of accident and emergency department – one doctor.

	A	B	C	D	E	F	G
1	Arrival rate		5		Completion rate		3
2							
3	Number of doctors		1				
4							
5	Patient	Time between each arrival (min)	Arrival of each patient (min)	Start of each consultation (min)	Length of each con-sultation (min)	Finishing time of each consultation (min)	Patient waiting time (min)
6	1	0	0	0	3	3	0
7	2	0	0	3	5	8	3
8	3	2	2	8	2	10	6
9	4	3	5	10	1	11	5
10	5	2	7	11	0	12	4
11	6	1	8	12	2	14	3
12	7	6	14	14	1	15	0
13	8	9	23	23	8	30	0
14	9	1	24	30	1	32	6
15	10	3	27	32	0	32	5
16	11	5	32	32	2	34	0
17	12	8	40	40	4	44	0
18	13	6	46	46	4	51	0
19	14	3	49	51	3	54	1
20	15	0	50	54	3	56	4
21	16	2	52	56	1	57	4
22	17	2	54	57	10	67	3
23	18	5	59	67	3	70	8
24	19	0	59	70	2	72	11
25	20	2	61	72	15	87	11
	Average total	3.21	3.051878		3.57		3.81

Time between each arrival (column B) represents the difference in time between each arrival. In 'queuing terms', this is often referred to as the 'inter-arrival time'.

Patients arrive at 'random'. This means that the probability that a patient arrives at any given instant of time is the same as the probability of an arrival at any other instant of time. This condition implies that the gap between each patient arrival follows a special mathematical pattern, known as the 'exponential probability distribution'. It is therefore likely that the inter-arrival times will be small. The proof of this is outside the scope of this chapter, but can be explored by consulting any standard statistical text. A suitable inter-arrival time can be generated using the formula

$$-1 * \text{Arrival rate} * \text{LN (RAND())}$$

The function LN is an Excel function. The effect of this is to convert the range of the random number function RAND() from 0...1 to the range $-\infty$ to 0. By multiplying by -1, we obtain a random value in the range 0 to ∞. Further explanation of this function can be obtained from mathematical texts. However, for this simulation, it is sufficient to know that it is important to use this function to cater for the irregularity of the patient arrivals.

Arrival time (column C) is the time that the next patient arrives. It is formed from the sum of the inter-arrival time and the previous arrival time.

Patient arrival time = Arrival time of previous patient + inter-arrival time

For example, from Table 11.6,

Start of each consultation (column D) represents the time that each patient starts their consultation. Towards the beginning of the period, this is very similar to arrival time. However, later in the simulation as the queue builds up, then the value is given by the finishing time of the previous consultation. In equation terms, this is formed using the IF statement in Excel.

Consultation start time: if the previous consultation finishes later than the appointment time, then this consultation starts when the previous consultation finishes: otherwise, this consultation starts at the scheduled appointment time, e.g. from Table 11.6

Length of each consultation (column E) is the length of time that each patient spends in consultation with the doctor. This is random (but of course actual or

'real' data can be used) and can be generated in a similar manner to the inter-arrival times (column B). The length of each consultation is generated by the formula

$$-1 * \text{Completion rate} * \text{LN (RAND())}$$

Finishing time of each consultation (column F) is given by adding the length of the consultation to the start time of that consultation.

Time consultation finished = Time consultation starts + consultation time

For example, in Excel terminology and using Table 11.6, this is given by

$$F9 = D9 + E9$$

Patient waiting time (column G) is the difference between the scheduled start of the consultation and the actual time that the consultation begins:

$$G9 = D9 - C9$$

| Patient waiting time | Actual start time of each consultation | Scheduled start time of each consultation |

A hospital scenario – model 2

In this particular scenario, I have widened the scope of the previous model (1) to consider the effects of more doctors being available to see incoming patients. In the example of Figure 11.5 and Table 11.7, the patient could see any of three doctors available for consultation.

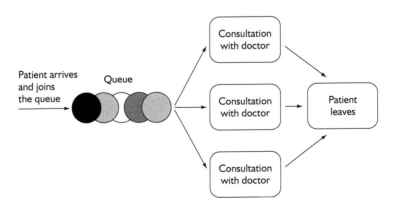

Figure 11.5 Hospital model with three doctors.

Table 11.7 Simulation of accident and emergency department – three doctors.

	A	B	C	D	E	F	G
1	Arrival rate	5				Completion rate	3
2							
3	Number of doctors		3				
4							
5	Patient	Time between each arrival (min)	Arrival of each patient (min)	Start of each consultation (min)	Length of each consultation (min)	Finishing time of each consultation (min)	Patient waiting time (min)
6	1	0	0	0	3	3	0
7	2	19	19	19	2	21	0
8	3	2	21	21	7	28	0
9	4	14	35	35	2	37	0
10	5	7	42	42	5	47	0
11	6	4	46	46	3	49	0
12	7	3	49	49	3	52	0
13	8	1	50	50	2	52	0
14	9	1	51	51	9	60	0
15	10	1	52	52	5	57	0
16	11	4	56	56	7	63	0
17	12	1	57	57	0	57	0
18	13	1	58	58	1	59	0
19	14	1	59	59	3	62	0
20	15	3	62	62	1	63	0
21	16	14	76	76	1	77	0
22	17	3	79	79	4	83	0
23	18	25	104	104	1	105	0
24	19	5	109	109	6	115	0
25	20	1	110	110	1	111	0
	Average total	5.79	5.5		3.25		0.00

When there are three doctors available, in 'queuing terminology' there are three service outlets. Therefore, for a given client, 'service' can begin either at the time that each patient arrives, or at the third largest finish time for preceding patients (as the other two will still be occupied). In equation form, this can be written as

Consultation begins:	either	if a doctor is available, then the consultation starts immediately
	or	if all the doctors are busy, then the consultation starts when one becomes free

When a patient arrives, any of the three doctors may be available to see them. Alternatively, as there are three doctors available for consultation, we may need to find the third largest value from the previous finishing times to determine the earliest time that one becomes available. As there may be more than one consultation under way at any given moment and the length of each consultation cannot be predicted, then the consultations may not finish in the order that they were started. In short then, what we are moving towards in this chapter is a scenario that may be more realistic. In this sense we have a simulation which has to cope with ever-increasing possibilities, uncertainties and probabilities.

Again in equation form we have an alternative way of expressing this. For example:

Take the largest value of: either   the current patient arrival time

                            or   third largest previous finishing time

In Excel terms, using Table 11.7, this can be written as

Cell D20   = MAX (patient arrival time, third largest from all previous finishing times)

             = MAX (C20, LARGE (F\$6:F19), 3)

In this case, cell D20 is the time that the next consultation is scheduled to start and cell C20 is the arrival time of the patient at the hospital. F\$6:F19 are cells showing the finishing times for previous patients, and the value 3 indicates that it is the third largest time that is required within that range. This model can be used for any number of similar 'service' outlets. For example, for five service outlets, we would look for the fifth largest finishing time of the preceding patients. The last parameter of the LARGE function would have the value of 5.

Running the simulation several times and varying the number of service outlets available, enables a comparison of results to be made (see Table 11.8). It is from such comparisons and reflections on the data that we can become more informed about alternative and possible courses of action. If reflection is to have a consequence, that is to say lead to some improvements in thinking, practice and the clinical contexts in which it takes place, then using the computer and the appropriate software to generate simulations of this kind can be an invaluable aid to learning.

A hospital scenario – model 3

We can develop this model still further by considering the real-life situation in accident and emergency. In an accident and emergency unit, patients arrive

125

Table 11.8 Comparison of the average length of consultation and average patient waiting time using various service areas.

	Average length of consultation	**Average patient waiting time**
I doctor	3.57	3.81
2 doctors	2.60	0.04
3 doctors	3.25	0.00
4 doctors	2.05	0.03
5 doctors	3.40	0.00

randomly, their condition is assessed and they are treated appropriately, dependent on their condition. This model includes a category for initial diagnosis and also illustrates the use of different service rates to take this into account. The model is shown in Figure 11.6.

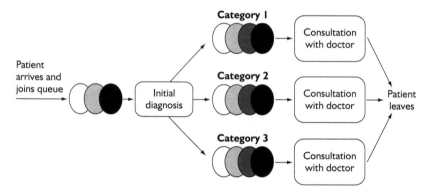

Figure 11.6 Hospital model with three different categories of patient injury.

Here I have made two assumptions: that patients arrive at random and their condition is categorised. Those patients in category 1, designated as the most serious, are treated in one area, with the completion rate being adjusted appropriately so as to allow for the consultation time being longer. Those patients in category 2, designated as serious, are treated in another area with a service rate adjusted appropriately so that the simulated consulting times are not quite as long as for category 1. Finally, those patients in category 3, designated as having minor injuries, are seen in another area with a service rate to ensure that the simulation reflects this adjustment and produces shorter consultation times.

Table 11.9 uses similar formulae to the previous model for inter-arrival time (column B) and arrival time (column C).

Patient type (column D) aims to simulate the random nature of the condition of arrivals. We need to generate random numbers of 1, 2 and 3 to denote the random nature of the severity of injuries. This can be achieved using the Excel function RANDBETWEEN (1, 3). Using this function, categories are allocated randomly to each patient. A development of this model could be to provide specific ratios for these categories to reflect specific trends and provide an even more 'lifelike' simulation: for example, 10% category 1 patients, 30% category 2 patients and 60% category 3 patients. Through the use of a LOOKUP table, as demonstrated in the doctor's waiting room model, the appropriate values could be simulated.

So how can the computer and information technology help us to make more effective decisions and enhance some of those environments in which healthcare professionals work? In healthcare settings, as in other educare professions, technological changes have brought about improvements in both practice and challenges. The healthcare worlds in which we work become more complex and turbulent. To practice, in a safe and accountable manner, reflection in and on action becomes essential. We need all the help we can get sometimes to try to make sense of what is happening around us. In the reflective practice literature we have the notions of critical friends and 'companions'. We have aids to learning from experience, such as critical incident analysis and learning journals. Information technology can also be seen as an aid to learning from experience. Technology will continue to change and develop, demanding a technologically literate population willing to embrace new methods of analysis (ways of seeing). The data contained in this chapter is included to show, if only briefly, what is possible. The aim is to illustrate how the computer can do much work for us and, in so doing, enable us to spend time reflecting on the results.

One of the positive things that I have tried to show here is that IT encourages the 'What if?' frame of mind. I have taken a number of situations, thought about their essential elements and used the computer to 'play' with them. The key is not to become enslaved by the software. We need to know what the software package can do for us. This is often time-consuming, but, in my experience, time often well worth investing. By 'playing' or 'manipulating' the variables, we can make the model more or less 'lifelike'. We can say things like, 'Well, here I need to increase the consultation time...' and 'Here I need to add in something else to make it more realistic'. At the end of the day the bottom line is an answer to the question, 'So what?'. There seems to be little merit for busy healthcare professionals to become bogged down with the technicalities of the package. What we need is the

Table 11.9 Spreadsheet for hospital model with three patient injury categories.

Arrival rate 1				Very serious — Completion rate 5				Serious — Completion rate 3				Not serious — Completion rate 2			
Patient	Time between arrivals	Arrival time	Severity of injury	Patient arrives	Waiting time (min)	Duration of consultation (min)	Finish time (min)	Patient arrives	Waiting time (min)	Duration of consultation (min)	Finish time (min)	Patient arrives	Waiting time (min)	Duration of consultation (min)	Finish time (min)
1	1	1	2		0	–	0	1	0	4	5				0
2	3	4	1	4	0	1	5				0				0
3	1	5	1	5	0	20	25				0				0
4	1	6	2				0	6	0	5	11				0
5	1	7	2				0	7	0	4	11				0
6	2	9	1	9	0	0	9				0				0
7	2	11	1	11	0	4	15				0				0
8	1	12	1	12	3	10	25				0				0
9	1	13	2				0	13	0	1	14				0
10	2	15	3				0				0	15	0	1	16
11	1	16	3				0				0	16	0	2	18
12	3	19	3				0				0	19	0	0	19
13	1	20	2				0	20	0	6	26				0
14	1	21	2				0	21	0	1	22				0
15	2	23	3				0				0	23	0	0	23
16	1	24	1	25	1	3	28				0				0
17	3	27	2				0	27	0	3	30				0
18	3	30	1	30	0	1	31				0				0
19	1	31	1	31	0	0	31				0				0
20	1	32	3				0				0	32	0	1	33
21	1	33	1	33	0	8	41				0				0
22	1	34	3				0				0	34	0	3	37
23	1	35	1	35	0	2	37				0				0
Total					3.64		0.0		0.0				0.00		

appropriate skill mix in our reflective teams (Ghaye and Lillyman, 2000) so that those who are computer literate help and support others either to input the data or (perhaps more importantly) interpret the results. Most colleagues are likely to be interested in the interpretation and discussion of results. For many this is where the action is: learning from the data, weighing up options in the light of this and planning future action. One of the most important attributes of reflective practices is to open up new possibilities for action, new ways of seeing and new sensitivities. I hope that the tables and figures in this chapter are a start in this direction.

An increasing number of courses for healthcare professionals involve the introduction of computers and the use of information technology. In schools, because of the implementation of the National Curriculum, a more computer literate population is emerging. Students pursuing post-school qualifications expect to use, and are expected to use, IT in the majority of their work, irrespective of subject discipline or vocational orientation. These will increasingly form part of our technologically aware population. These students (which of course include nursing students) are maturing with an expectation of using IT to enrich their learning and to use it as an aid to effective and efficient learning.

Arguably, it is those people already in employment that face the biggest challenge. They need to have similar expectations from IT. However, through lack of knowledge, a large proportion of these people still see IT as an 'add-on' to their decision making and organisation. They need support, guidance and encouragement to embrace fully the technological opportunities available. Dean (1998) comments that 'the inclusion of technology and technological innovations should be another tool to aid the planning of individualised patient care'. The arguments for the increasing use of technology in analysis and planning are strong but rely on a working knowledge of information technology 'without feeling intimidated by the computer' (Ashworth, 1990; Mann, 1992). Healthcare professionals need to rise to this challenge – our children, the patients of tomorrow, are depending on them.

References

Ashworth, P. (1990) High technology and humanity for intensive care. *Intensive Care Nursing*, **6**, 150–60.

Dean, B. (1998) Reflections on technology: increasing the science but diminishing the art of nursing? *Accident and Emergency Nursing*, **6**, 200–6.

Ghaye, T. and Lillyman, S. (2000) *Reflection: Principles and Practice for Healthcare Professionals*. Quay Books, London.

Lighthill, J. (ed.) (1978) *Newer Users of Mathematics*. Penguin, London.

Mann, R. (1992) Preserving humanity in an age of technology. *Intensive Critical Care Nursing*, **8**, 54–9.

Rothery, A. (1990) *Modelling with Spreadsheets*. Chartwell-Bratt Publishing, London.

Recommended reading

Dennis, T. L. and Dennis, L. B. (1991) *Management Science*, pp. 544–627. West Publishing, California.

Nickerson, R. C. (1998) *Business Information Systems*, pp. 231–9. Addison-Wesley, Massachusetts.

Index